CHOOSE *to* THRIVE

Open Up to Vitality, Prosperity & Equanimity

SUSAN SMITH JONES, PhD
FOREWORD BY DAVID CRADDOCK

Books to UPLIFT
Rejuvenating Your Health & Enriching Your Life

The health suggestions and recommendations in this book are based on the training, research and personal experiences of the author. Because each person and each situation is unique, the author and publisher encourage the reader to check with his or her physician or other health professional before using any procedure outlined in this book. Neither the author nor the publisher is responsible for any adverse consequences resulting from any of the suggestions in this book.

Published by Books to UPLIFT
Los Angeles, CA

Cover and book design: Gary A. Rosenberg
Interior photos by AdobeStock.com and Susan Jones

ISBN: 978-0-9991492-4-9

For further information and permission approval, contact:

Books to UPLIFT, PO Box 49215, Los Angeles, CA 90049,
Attn. Manager

To order additional copies of this book,
please visit: **SusanSmithJones.com**

This book is dedicated in loving memory of my glorious mom, June, who, by her shining example, taught me about unconditional love, living with passion, following my heart, never giving up on my dreams and making the Golden Rule my default position every day.

And it's also joyfully dedicated to my two wonderful sisters, June and Jamie, who continually inspire me with their loving, generous hearts and the way they celebrate with gusto and vivacity their family, friends and life.

… And finally to you, for reading this book and for choosing to create your very best life and thrive—to experience the highest level of health, joy, love, peace, passion, success and balance possible. I salute your great adventure.

QUOTES FOR INSPIRATION
& MOTIVATION

*Most people work so hard at living
that they forget how to live fully.*
—SUSAN SMITH JONES

If you can dream it, you can do it.
—WALT DISNEY

*Do not go where the path may lead. Go instead
where there is no path and leave a trail.*
—RALPH WALDO EMERSON

*Have the vision to see, the faith to believe, and
the courage to act on your intuitive guidance.*
—SUSAN SMITH JONES

*Take a step of faith and no matter how you
feel, agree with God that He loves you.*
—JOYCE MEYER

Contents

PART 4: Open Up to Prosperity: Turning Your Dreams Into Reality

Foreword

By David Craddock

WHEN DR. SUSAN WROTE HER BOOK, *Invest in Yourself with Exercise: Tactics to Build the Exercise Habit and Enrich & Energize Your Workouts*, and sent it to me in England to peruse, I felt honored and her suggestions and detailed program in the book helped me upgrade my exercise program, tone up my muscles and lose the last ten pounds I was carrying around my waist. After reading it, we discussed some of the book's contents and she could tell how enthusiastic I was about this book. So, imagine my delight when Susan then asked me, during this telephone conversation, if I would be willing to write the Foreword for the book, and I gladly accepted the offer. If you haven't yet gotten a copy of this health-enriching book (and I encourage you to do so soon because it will change your health and life for the better!), you can still read my Foreword in its entirety on Susan's website.

Susan's writings and holistic health counseling with me have had a very positive influence in my life. And if you haven't read my Foreword for *Invest in Yourself with Exercise*, I will briefly encapsulate what I wrote previously so you can see how I met Susan and how fortunate I was when I asked her if she would guide me on bolstering my personal health program to which she accepted.

For almost 10 years, she has been my holistic health guru and coach, teaching me how to create vibrant health and get fit and strong. As a result, I now feel about 30 years younger than I did just a few years ago, and people tell me that I look better than I have in decades. My work with Susan has given me the fountain of youth and vitality. But I'm getting ahead of myself. Let me start back at the beginning.

It was early June 2009 when my health seemed to be at an all-time low. In England where I live, I focused much of my time on my career and didn't put time into my health needs. I had terrible allergies (they had plagued me for 30 years) and I definitely needed to lose lots of weight. I didn't know where to turn for the holistic help I desired.

There's a saying that . . . *When the student is ready, the teacher will appear.* One day I was talking to my mum (Marjorie) about my health issues. As always, in her positive approach to life, she said to me, "You will find the answers you seek." That same day, I got in the mail some information about a 3-Day Holistic Health Conference that would be held in London featuring many world-renowned health and human potential speakers. They were all experts in their fields from around the world, but the only one that truly caught my attention was the speaker Susan Smith Jones, PhD.

She was giving three presentations on all aspects of healing and rejuvenating the body, mind and spirit, and I knew at that moment that I needed to attend.

Before I got this conference information, I had already known about Susan's work. Marjorie and I had been reading many of her articles in magazines in the UK and America, we had a few of her many books, and I saw her on a TV talk show when I was in New York City. On a few occasions, we even heard her on BBC radio talk shows in the UK and saw her on some British TV talk shows. We always enjoyed her holistic, practical and positive approach to wellness, balanced living and creating our best lives.

Marjorie and I attended the conference together in London and were not disappointed. Susan's three presentations were life-changing for us. One was about fitness and simple, sound ways to create a strong, lean body and how to stay motivated to exercise for life. Another one of her talks was about nutrition and how to fuel the body with the healthiest foods and break unhealthy food habits. And her third presentation was all about the essential "healthy living extras," as Susan would always refer to them—the other wellness components that can make a profound difference in how we look and feel, such as sleep, water hydration, stress reduction, meditation and prayer-time, positive relationships, an attitude of gratitude, why and how to declutter one's home and office, simple ways to upgrade our living spaces, time outside in nature and more.

I couldn't get enough of her talks. Throughout all three, I was taking copious notes as I sat in the front row each time. During the question and answer sessions of each talk, I was always the first person to raise my hand and ask for clarification on things she discussed. Susan was always patient, thoughtful and sensitive to my questions and other people's questions in the room. It was clear from her three standing ovations that everyone else in the room appreciated her three talks as much as I did.

At the end of the third presentation, I asked Susan if she would be willing to meet with me privately in the lecture hall after everyone left to talk about some of my mum's and my personal health concerns and possibly even agree to work with me. During that first session with her, I knew, for sure, that I was guided to the best teacher for me. Susan is knowledgeable and kind, has a wonderful sense of humor and knows how to inspire, motivate and empower her clients. When I asked if she would agree to coach me on how to get healthy and fit, she agreed and suggested that I fly to Santa Monica (Los Angeles) with Marjorie (she was 80 at the time) the following late December 2009/early January 2010 to "end the year and start the new year off with a positive commitment to health and youthful vitality," she said. We started the counseling process the last half of 2009 with telephone conference calls weekly where she would answer my many health and fitness questions.

This trip and time with Susan turned out to be a godsend for Marjorie and me. The first morning, the three of us were sitting in the Fig restaurant at the Fairmont Miramar Hotel in Santa Monica where we were staying, and during this early morning breakfast, she was going over the personal food and exercise diary I had kept for the previous two weeks. She asked me to write down every single thing that I ate, and the water I drank, and not to forget anything—no matter how small. Additionally, I had to write down any physical exercise I did, too, which was only one day of a brief 15-minute walk between two meetings in London (of course, I now choose to be physically active every day in some way!).

As I watched her looking over my diary of notes, which also included Marjorie's food diary and no exercise at all to report, Susan was very quiet. She kept writing notes on the sides of my pages, and I did notice her eyes get bigger as she read on. My mum and I tapped each other under the table wondering what Susan was thinking. For about six minutes or so (probably the longest six minutes of my life, aside from our first power walk that same afternoon on the bluff!), she said nothing while she was examining all the foods I ate from the two previous weeks written in my lifestyle diary along with my nonexistent exercise routine.

I was getting more nervous by the second. What was she going to say, I thought? Was she wishing that we had not come to Los Angeles to be coached by her? "Please Susan, say something so I know there's hope for my goal of getting healthy and fit," I pondered inside my head. Then, she finally looked up, smiled a big grin at my mum and me, and said in the most positive tone the following: "Okay David and Marjorie, we have lots of work to do and I have loads to teach you both, but I am confident that you will both leave here healthier than either of you have ever been in your lives. I also know that you will feel so motivated, inspired and empowered that you'll want to continue with this same program I'll be giving you when you get home. So let's get started by both of you telling me, since you've looked at the Fig's breakfast menu for over five minutes, what you'd like to order now that's healthy." She also sensed that we were both a little nervous not knowing what to expect.

And that was the beginning of our life-changing work with Susan. She was positive right from the start and has never wavered in all the time to be anything other than optimistic, enthusiastic, forthright and always sensitive to both of us. And by the way, even though I thought she wasn't aware of our nervousness and how my mum and

I tapped each other's knees under the table, Susan mentioned to us that there's nothing to be anxious about. She would give us both one of the most wonderful, positive experiences we've ever had while we both get healthy. One of the things I learned about Susan that first visit, and it's still true to this day, is that she's aware of everything around her, likes to live in the present moment with optimistic enthusiasm and is ever so eager to help others feel good about themselves and create their best, healthiest lives.

For two weeks we stayed at the lovely Fairmont Miramar Hotel on the bluff across from the Santa Monica beach and every day and evening, Susan worked with both Marjorie and me, teaching us about all of the principles and practices of a healthy lifestyle. According to Susan, I needed to lose about 75 pounds and get healthy (before I arrived, I thought I only needed to lose about 30 pounds!), and Marjorie needed to gain about six pounds and become mobile again. Mum arrived in a wheelchair, barely able to walk on her own, and I resolved

to achieve significant improvement in my health and was open to any guidance Susan would be giving me.

On that first day after breakfast, Susan took both of us to the hotel's beautiful, fully-loaded gym to do weight training and use the aerobic equipment, which we did *every day* we were there. She took me hiking in the mountains of Santa Monica, for long walks on the beach, and taught us many other enjoyable ways to exercise that were actually pleasurable such as exercising in the swimming pool in the beautiful sunshine of Santa Monica (quite different from England's cold weather!). All the time, she would talk to us in great detail and educate us about why we should or should not do things a certain way, and yes, I continued to takes lots of notes daily. She said that when we got back home to England, both of us needed a strong understanding of all the principles of why we eat or don't eat specific foods, or do certain things, so we would stay inspired and motivated when Susan wasn't with us. She even showed us how to order off restaurant menus for healthy selections, how to shop at grocery stores for the healthiest foods, made sure we were well-hydrated, slept each night for eight hours and she made the process of getting healthy really fun! Susan encouraged us to meditate, relax and chill out when things got stressful; she gave us reasons why and tips on how to declutter our living spaces (including our homes, offices, cars, etc.); she also covered in detail how to sleep like a baby each night and took us to her home and gave us private cooking lessons.

And if that were not enough, Susan, in her spare time, works with clients on upgrading and refurbishing their homes, both exterior and interior. So I showed her photos of my home in England and she guided me on beautiful and sophisticated changes I could make to my home (inside and out), gardens and surroundings. Because of her terrific suggestions, I added shutters, a new front door and new windows, new gutters and down spouts, new walkways, hanging flower baskets, new garden flowers and a picket fence to my home, and people in my neighborhood often stop by to tell me how great my home now looks.

Back to Santa Monica: one of my favorite exercises in the hotel's gym was the rowing machine. Susan taught me how to row with good form to prevent injury and get the maximum benefits and now I row several times weekly back in England. It's my favorite aerobic activity in the gym because it's great as a cardio workout, but it is also an excellent endurance- and strength-builder.

When we arrived in Los Angeles, Susan promised she would give us both her recipe for the "fountain of youth" and teach us how to maintain it when we got back home to England. Well, she did accomplish this and so much more. Marjorie arrived in Santa Monica unable to walk without assistance and 14 days later, mum built up to walking three miles a day without help, and was gobsmacked at how great she felt. In fact, she didn't want to leave Susan or the sunshine. Marjorie had never stepped foot in a gym before this trip, and she grew to love the weight training because she could see her strength increasing by the day. Susan patiently helped her feel comfortable with the weights and aerobic machines and watched her every movement.

Mum was over-the-moon with joy and vitality when she left and had gained six pounds, exactly what she needed. Oh, by the way, when we got back to England, Marjorie joined our local gym and kept weight training regularly. In fact, the local newspaper in our town in England wrote an article about Marjorie and her weight training, as she was the oldest member of the gym.

By the way, Susan's #1 secret to looking younger is to smile and she's right. As a result of my health and fitness achievements, I am smiling all the time now and people tell me often how youthful I look.

When I arrived under Susan's holistic care on the first day, I noticed how tired I felt after our one-mile jog/power walk on the bluff overlooking the Santa Monica Bay. By the last few days, I was weight training for one hour, hiking the steep mountains in Santa Monica for three hours with Susan, and jogging on the soft sand of the beach for another workout—all in the same day! In-between these arduous workouts, we would stretch often to increase flexibility.

Another one of her promises to me was that if I would follow her allergy program for four months when I got home, I would be rid of my allergies for good after 30 years of this annoyance. She was right. Within just under four months of taking some specific nutritional supplements and clean-ing up my diet, keeping more hydrated and getting more sleep, my allergies were gone and have never returned.

I returned back to England 13 pounds lighter in 14 days, and we ate all day long. It was like a miracle to me! I learned a whole new way of eating— choosing delicious high fiber, plant-based, nutrient-rich foods. Those two weeks under Susan's guidance changed my health and life for the better. Since my visit with Susan early January 2010, I've continued with her healthy living program, have lost almost 80 pounds through regular exercise and a healthy diet, and she checks in with me regularly to fine-tune my personal plan of action for optimum health and youthful vitality . . . always. I can honestly say that I have never felt better in my life than I do right now.

Presently, I eat a clean, healthy, lean diet and choose organic foods, whenever possible. It's easy to order at restaurants now because most menus have healthy alternatives or the chefs are willing and happy to prepare healthy dishes for me.

Because of Susan's positive teachings, combined with my desire to stay healthy, happy, strong and fit well into older age, I now usually workout in the local gym in town four to six days weekly. Susan even came over and helped me set up a home gym with some aerobic equipment (yes, it includes a rowing machine), a couple benches, dumbbells and other machines (and yes, she even guided me on how to spruce up my home's interior and to declutter and organize everything better!). This way when my schedule is really tight with work, conferences and meetings, I still have a place in my home to exercise. And now, when I travel to locations around the world to give my lectures and presentations and to meet with clients, I always take my fitness clothes to get in power walks or jogs; I find hotels that have in-house gyms; and I pack in my luggage exercise bands which weigh next to nothing that are simple to use in the hotel room.

Something else changed in me when I lost all my extra weight. I cared more about my personal appearance, how I dressed and what grooming I did to look and feel my best. I've learned from Susan that this is very common. When one carries around lots of extra weight for years, as I did, you often simply dress for comfort, wearing the same sloppy clothes that are loose fitting and don't hang well on the body. That's what I did for a couple of decades. I was embarrassed with being so overweight and didn't put much thought into how I dressed or looked. As you can imagine, after I lost about 80 pounds, nothing in my clothes closets fit me any more—not my suits, jackets, sweaters (we say jumpers in the UK), shirts, exercise clothes, and even my shoes.

On this one particular visit to Los Angeles for several business meetings and to confer with Susan on upgrading my fitness and nutrition program, I turned on the TV and watched one of my favorite programs—Joel Osteen's show and listened to his discussion on *Commitment to Excellence*. In his talk, he mentioned we should all strive for excellence in every area of our lives, including our living spaces (homes, offices and cars), in how we dress and look, in what we eat, in how we exercise and in how we care for our bodies with grooming. His words truly inspired me.

As luck would have it, that same afternoon, seemingly out of nowhere because I hadn't told Susan about Joel's sermon topic, she showed me her impressive album of "before" and "after" photos of countless client makeovers. Doing *Whole-Body Rejuvenation Makeovers* with clients of all ages—from pre-teens to seniors to help people look and feel their best from the inside out, top to bottom is another one of her many talents and gifts. The photos were amazing, to say the least. Everyone looked younger, healthier and more vibrant in the "after" photos with different style clothing, hairstyles, good grooming and reduction of weight. Knowing that I'm always in the best of hands with Susan, I asked her if she would please do a Whole-Body Rejuvenation Makeover on me since none of my clothes fit me anymore.

So for the next two days, from head-to-toe, she rejuvenated my body and appearance and knew exactly what I needed to do. She had a hairstylist give me a different haircut (with the little hair I have left on my head these days!); I purchased and learned how to use moisturizers on my face and around my eyes; I experienced my first manicure and pedicure (which I now do monthly in England); and she took me shopping to a few different stores in Santa Monica, Brentwood and Beverly Hills for an entire new collection of suits, jackets, shirts, fitness attire, belts, shoes and more. Even my watches and rings needed to be made smaller with my 80-pound weight loss.

To say she's an expert on rejuvenation, clothes styling and grooming, and to say that I was delighted with the results, would both be understatements. She gave me an entire course in those two days on

what it means to "Dress for Success," whether wearing business suits, casual jackets or exercise clothes. In the past, mainly because of my hefty weight issues, I just wore anything that fit, paying no attention to how I looked. But there's an idiom in America that "clothes make the man." Susan helped me to understand that people often judge others according to the way they dress.

I also learned, firsthand, that dressing well helps people to be more successful. When I put on those new clothes that fit me perfectly, were more sophisticated and classy, I felt more confident and debonair, and these feelings translated into my business life. Of course, it didn't hurt that all my colleagues, friends and family, for the first time in my life, when I started wearing all of these great-fitting, stylish clothes, kept telling me that I've never looked better or younger in my life. People continued to tell me that I looked about 30 years younger than my age. What Susan did for my health and appearance has been priceless and added such joy, confidence and equanimity to my life. I am now thriving in my life in every way, thanks to Susan's support and expertise.

As Susan told me in those rejuvenation makeover days, you never know when a TV show may want to interview you, or you get a request to go to the Parliament for a meeting or you need to meet with influential business people and celebrities with last-minute invitations. So you always want to look your best, exude excellence and feel confident, self-assured, refined and sophisticated—and ready at a moment's notice to say YES to life's adventures and not put them off because you're not feeling confident with how you look and feel. Now I shudder to think back to how I used to dress and didn't care at all about grooming or my appearance and am deeply grateful to Susan for showing me how to be a class act with sartorial elegance.

In all her sagacity, Susan always reminds me that . . . "When you commit to something like an exercise program, don't let your excuses get in your way. You must follow through on your commitment to fitness and arrange your personal circumstances so that your lifestyle totally supports your commitment." She'd often tell me to . . . "Do the things you need to do to order your life, eliminate non-essentials and focus on what is important."

Susan helped me to understand that if we don't have health, we lose our enjoyment and appreciation of life. It is truly our greatest wealth. She taught me that I am the president and CEO of my body and life and it's up to me to take great care of my body. Here's something she emphasized often to me: "To become master of your outer life, you must first become master of your inner world—CEO of your mind. Teach your mind how to think differently: how to be calm, loving, courageous and optimistic. The body reflects the mind and the mind reflect the spirit; all three are connected and holistic health incorporates the loving care of the whole person. Eating healthy foods gives you a more positive attitude. Choosing to be grateful for your miraculous body makes it easier to exercise and get ample sleep at night. So each day make your health a top priority and take loving care of your body with nutritious foods, daily exercise, positive living habits and a cheerful attitude." I will never forget her teachings and now in my work with other people, I often share some of the health- and life-enriching teachings I learned from Susan and am still learning to this day.

So when she asked me if I would write the Foreword for the other book, *Invest in Yourself with Exercise*, it was my great pleasure. In the pages of that informative and uplifting book, you'll learn from Susan the importance of exercise for overall high-level wellness; how to get the most from your workouts; ways to stay motivated to exercise; tips to prevent exercise boredom, burnout and injury; the best exercises to look younger, bolster energy and lose weight; how to fight excess fat by mastering your metabolism; how to incorporate prayer-walking to enhance mental and spiritual health; ways to turn dreams into reality; the power of choice; and much more.

"An investment in yourself and in your health," as Susan repeated to me often in our training and teaching sessions, "is the best investment you can make." That book will inspire, motivate and empower you, too.

So now, fast forward to this book *Choose to Thrive*. A couple years ago, Susan started working with me on much more than my health and fitness program. In addition to attending many of her workshops around the world and cooking classes, she has been working with me on other principles and practices for high quality living and, on a personal note, helping me cope and deal with my sadness and grief over my mother's passing.

From Susan, I've learned about the physiology of stress and how unmanaged chronic stress wreaks havoc on the entire body; I learned a variety of stress management techniques including deep breathing, visualization and meditation, which for Susan and me as Christians is based on inspiring verses within the Bible; her teachings have reinforced my long-held beliefs of why it's so important to make my word count, make my word gold, and to go the extra mile and always be open to learning new things and testing new concepts; and I also learned how to be more effective in all of my business dealings when relating to others and managing transactions. Susan always emphasizes the importance of making a commitment, staying disciplined in achieving goals and following through on your words with actions. Susan demystified how to live a balanced lifestyle, invite equanimity into my daily routines and be prosperous in mind first to then see it manifest in my life. In short, Susan has made a positive difference in every area of my life and, as a result, my business, home life and health are all thriving.

So just over a year ago, in one of our healthy living conference calls, I thanked her for showing me in multiple ways how to truly thrive in every area of my life. I told her I now understood how it needs to be a holistic approach with the body, mind and spirit all supporting each other and in balance, as she always taught me and emphasized in our sessions together and by telephone.

It was at that moment that I casually mentioned to her, half seriously and half jokingly, that "Susan, you should write another book entitled *Choose to Thrive: Open Up to Vitality, Prosperity & Equanimity*." For about 30 seconds after hearing my suggestion, she was quiet. Then she enthusiastically said, "I love your idea David and, YES, indeed, that's what I'll write about in my next book. But I have one condition. Will you write another Foreword for this new book when I finish it?" With alacrity, I responded that it would be my honor to work with her again on another Foreword, so that brings us to the present and this new Foreword.

Susan's books and other writings inspire people around the world, especially me. She's one of those rare authors who writes the way she talks. She shines in her ability to take complex ideas and complicated research and distill it all down to easy-to-comprehend and understand, practical guidance and motivation.

Since writing the Foreword for *Invest in Yourself with Exercise*, countless people have asked me privately... *"What is Susan really like, since you know her so well and she has worked with you for years? What can you tell me about Susan that others may not know?"* This is something I can share with you from personal experience of working with Susan privately, attending many of her lectures and workshops, taking many of her cooking and holistic health classes, and spending countless hours with her exercising, hiking, going to the gym and eating meals out together.

Susan's dynamic presence is an inspiration to all who desire to not only talk, but also walk the way of wellness, balance and living life fully alive. Her enthusiasm, experience and her vast knowledge of the current fields of balanced living, nutrition, exercise and holistic health are great gifts to everyone she encounters. She has a way of living the principles she speaks about that causes others, myself included, to desire to follow the path of healthy living. Susan is a vibrant expression of health, aliveness and zest for living.

A consummate motivational lecturer, she is the kind of speaker that every program director wishes for but rarely ever experiences. She is always filled with enthusiasm and it's catching. Radiantly beautiful inside and out, she's one of the most amazing people I've ever met—a perfectly balanced person of inner strength, kindness, humor and a peaceful equanimity. She's a storehouse of life-altering knowledge that is up-to-date; she's a Renaissance woman and gifted teacher who brings together modern research and ageless wisdom in all of her work, including her workshops, books, audio programs or her dynamic radio and television interviews.

There is something else about Susan that is difficult to define. It's her total consciousness of love, joy and well-being. I host seminars in the UK, America and internationally for my *Time for Investment* company, and invite world-renowned speakers to talk about finance, investing, the economy, saving money, credit card debt, prosperity, abundance and why health is the greatest wealth (of course, those health talks are always given by Susan!). We have all had seminar presenters or attended a seminar with presenters who knew the material, but behind the scenes we were disappointed to find that they didn't really live the truth they were teaching. I assure you that Dr. Susan embodies the truth she shares.

And I might add, what a sense of humor she has—it's delightful and makes me happy every time I am with her. Susan helped bring out my sense of humor by watching how she talks to others, presents her motivational lectures and deals with her own stresses. In every

encounter she has with others, she always tries to build someone up and find a way to tickle their funny bone. One of the first quotes she said to me when my mum and I first worked with her in Santa Monica late 2009/early 2010 was by Maya Angelou, who said... *People will forget what you said, people will forget what you did, but people will never forget how you made them feel.* How true that is! People tell me often

how good they always feel in Susan's presence. She's a practical joker, yes indeed, and loves to laugh a lot. Susan taught me early on when I first worked with her about the power of relaxation to rejuvenate and restore the soul, the therapeutic effects and relationship-enhancing qualities of sharing fun and enjoyment together, and how we need to smile and laugh more, and she is the perfect example. Very little in life makes Susan upset and feel totally stressed out. Her attitude is always about seeing the best in everyone and everything and finding reasons to laugh as much as possible. No wonder her nickname is "Sunny." Let me give you one of many countless examples of Susan's jovial, comical and light-hearted attitude... no matter the circumstances.

She was giving a cooking class to about 20 people in her home. This was the first class since she totally refurbished her kitchen and large adjoining family room with new cabinets, wood floors, shiplap on the walls, new paint everywhere, wood beam ceilings, new area rugs, etc.—everything was new and beautiful and she was so excited for her guests to see how she decorated it all. It happened to be St. Patrick's Day and during this lunch-time class, everything was laid out on the massive marble island in the center of her kitchen and the guests were either seated around the island or standing behind. All of the foods made during the previous hour were displayed on the island to eat shortly. But first, she wanted to finish her cooking and nutrition demonstrations by making a healthy and delicious green smoothie. So into the blender went fresh almond milk (that was just made fresh earlier), frozen blueberries and raspberries, a frozen banana, one cucumber, a tablespoon of flaxseeds, some baby leaf spinach, celery, a dash of cinnamon and ice cubes. She blended it all in the 72-ounce jar, which was filled to the brim with scrumptious, creamy, totally blended green smoothie. She took off the lid and was about to give us all a sample when she realized that she forgot to put in some kale. Susan then asked one of the guests seated at the end island stool to get the kale from the refrigerator and finish making the smoothie while she went to use the bathroom and quickly changed her clothes before eating.

So while Susan was at the far end of her home in her bedroom suite, this guest put some kale into the blender and you've probably already guessed what was about to happen next. She forgot to put the lid on the blender after the kale went in and she pressed the start button that was already on high speed before anyone had a chance to tell her to put the lid back on top first. With the force of an angry volcano, this green 72-ounce smoothie shot up to the high ceiling above, drenching all the shiplap in "green goodness" and also covering the entire island with all of the food, the floors, the area rugs, the walls and most of the people watching, too. Everyone was in shock and didn't even know what to say so most of the guests were totally silent and, at the same time, very nervous because Susan's kitchen and family room was just refurbished and now everything was green.

Susan danced out of her bedroom and down the hall singing a song and was eager to sit down with everyone and start eating all of the foods that were just created the previous hour. Then she saw what happened and everyone was staring at her and Susan, to the surprise and delight of everyone, started laughing so hard that everyone else started laughing. It definitely relieved the tension in the room. But Susan couldn't stop laughing for about 3 minutes; in fact, she was laughing so hard that she was tearing up. Then she said joyfully, "It's my fault, I forgot to tell you to put the lid on, and how beautiful is this! Today is St. Patrick's Day and now there's no need to decorate because everything is already green." Well, that made all of the guests laugh even more. Everyone joined in with the cleaning up and Susan turned on some great music and ordered some food to be delivered from a local restaurant for everyone to eat together, since all of the dishes/meals on the island ready to sample and eat were covered in green smoothie.

That, in a nutshell, is Susan. She's filled with vitality, joy, happiness, optimism and celebration for everyone she meets and for life itself. And that's what shines through in the pages of this book *Choose to Thrive*. You will feel like you are visiting Susan at her home and sitting at her kitchen table as she visits with you and shares her pearls of wisdom to guide you on how to experience true aliveness, how to live more fully and how to thrive in all areas of your life. As you read this upbeat book, you will feel like Susan is your friend, too, because she's truly a friend to everyone.

I have one word of warning for you. Once you meet Susan, or read this dynamic book, or listen to or read her other wonderful, uplifting books and audio programs, you'll be inspired to make some major lifestyle changes for the better. So, get yourself ready—for a healthier and more joyful, peaceful new you will emerge once you've met this glorious Renaissance lady through the pages of this book.

In conclusion, all of Susan's books are terrific, but this one is now my favorite because her sage advice, practical tips and buoyant, vivacious personality sparkle forth on every page. And from my personal experience of working with Susan for almost a decade, and seeing her firsthand interactions with others, I can say for certain that Susan has never met a stranger and can speak with anyone from all walks of life. She has a calm and peaceful demeanor, the humor of a comedian, the curiosity of a child, the wisdom of a favorite grandparent and the non-judgment of a best friend—all rolled into one. *Choose to Thrive* will also bless your life, as it has for me many times over, in countless ways and put you on the path to high-level vitality, success, prosperity, equanimity and a balanced, joy-filled life. Enjoy!

David Craddock, MA (Oxon), BA (Hons)
DavidCraddock.com
TimeForInvestment.com

It is easy for us to get caught up in looking at how far we have to go in reaching our goals instead of celebrating how far we have come.

—JOYCE MEYER

Epigraphs

On these beginning pages, and throughout the book, I'll share with you a few of my favorite uplifting and positive quotes that have inspired me over the years during my great adventure—my life.

Whatever is true, whatever is honorable and worthy of respect, whatever is right and confirmed by God's word, whatever is pure and wholesome, whatever is lovely and brings peace, whatever is admirable and of good repute; if there is any excellence, if there is anything worthy of praise, think continually on these things [center your mind on them, and implant them in your heart]. The things which you have learned and received and heard and seen in me, practice these things [in daily life], and the God [who is the source] of peace and well-being will be with you.

—Philippians 4:8–9 (AMP)

So long as we believe in our heart of hearts that our capacity is limited and we grow anxious and unhappy, we are lacking in faith. One who truly trusts in God has no right to be anxious about anything.

—Paramahansa Yogananda

Each patient carries his own doctor inside him.

—Albert Sweitzer

My life belongs to the whole community, and as long
as I live, it is my privilege to do for it whatsoever I
can. I want to be thoroughly used up when I die, for
the harder I work, the more I live. I rejoice in life
for its own sake. Life is no 'brief candle' to me. It is a
sort of splendid torch which I have got hold of for the
moment, and I want to make it burn as brightly as
possible before handing it on to future generations.

—GEORGE BERNARD SHAW

There is a principle which is a bar against information,
which is proof against all argument, and which
cannot fail to keep a man in everlasting ignorance.
That principle is Contempt prior to investigation.

—HERBERT SPENCER

Of course I love everyone I meet. How could I fail
to? Within everyone is the spark of God. I am not
concerned with racial or ethnic background or the color
of one's skin; all people look to me like shining lights!

—PEACE PILGRIM

Remember always that you not only
have the right to be an individual,
you also have an obligation to be one.

—ELEANOR ROOSEVELT

Hope is one of the best ways to shed light
on the process of unfolding miracles—and
it's part of the ongoing miracle itself.

—THOMAS KINKADE

I slept and dreamt that life was joy.
I awoke and saw that life was service.
I acted and behold service was joy.

—RABINDRANATH TAGORE

Anxiety is the mark of spiritual insecurity.

—THOMAS MERTON

It isn't enough to talk about peace.
One must believe in it. And it isn't enough
to believe in it. One must work at it.

—ELEANOR ROOSEVELT

It is one of the most beautiful compensations of this life
that no man can sincerely try to help another without
helping himself. . . . Serve and thou shall be served.

—RALPH WALDO EMERSON

Live in the present. Do the things you know
need to be done. Do all the good you can
each day. The future will unfold.

—PEACE PILGRIM

Do not conform to the pattern of this world,
but be transformed by the renewing of your mind.

—ROMANS 12:2

The doctor of the future will give no medicine, but will
interest his patients in the care of the human frame,
in diet, and in the cause and prevention of disease.

—THOMAS A. EDISON

This is the true joy in life, the being used for a
purpose recognized by yourself as a mighty one . . .
the being a force of Nature instead of a feverish
selfish little clod of ailments and grievances
complaining that the world will not
devote itself to making you happy.

—GEORGE BERNARD SHAW

Preface

*Life is a paradise for those who love
many things with passion.*
—LEO BUSCAGLIA

*'Tis the good reader that makes the good book; in every
book he finds passages which seem confidences or asides
hidden from all else and unmistakably meant for his ear;
the profit of all books is according to the sensibility of the
reader; the profoundest thought or passion sleeps as in a
mine, until it is discovered by an equal mind and heart.*
—RALPH WALDO EMERSON

WHAT A JOY IT IS TO HAVE THIS OPPORTUNITY to share my life
and experiences on simple ways to renew your life, to create a healthy,
peaceful, and balanced lifestyle and to thrive in all of your endeavors.
To thrive means to grow and develop well and vigorously, to prosper
and to flourish (i.e. a thriving economy). Isn't that what we all want
in our lives?

Writing a book is, undeniably, an extraordinary, sometimes difficult, yet always rewarding journey. For me, it's a process of discipline,
dedication, perseverance and commitment, and, of course, renders
life-changing self-realization. Like my inviting early morning hikes in
my local Santa Monica Mountains—breathtaking, bucolic, eye-open-
ing trails winding up and down with a combination of arduous and
easy maneuvers—writing a book is a similar experience, just longer. As
the days, weeks, months and years come and go, the solitary process

of transmuting intuitive thoughts, ideas, research and personal experience into a format accessible to readers fills me with ineffable joy sprinkled with intermittent heartache and immense passion. So it is with verve and enthusiasm, I share with you this book and my adventure. It is my greatest hope that my words and suggestions throughout this book will inspire, uplift, motivate and empower you to make more conscious choices to create your very best life.

As you read through the pages, I want you to feel like we're sitting across from each other while I talk to you personally. I already know that we have a few things in common, since you've chosen to read a book on radiant health and vitality and, perhaps, to strive to be the best you can be. I am eager to share with you this "choose to thrive" program that has created success for thousands of people worldwide. It can do the same for you.

The power of choice is ours. It's up to each of us to create a meaningful, healthy life for ourselves. Sometimes that requires moving out of our comfort zone and the familiar in order to reach the acme of unbounded vitality. Yes, there is a way of eating, thinking, moving

and living, one that heals our bodies, promotes radiant health and rejuvenates our lives.

Imagine, if you can, a life without ever feeling sick—without aches, pains or fatigue. Imagine never getting colds or the flu or depression. Imagine waking up each day—bouncing out of bed—eager to experience life's great adventures with joy and passion. Imagine not being tempted by unhealthful foods or recreational drugs, or succumbing to noisome addictions. Imagine being your ideal weight and having people consistently praise you on how beautiful/handsome and youthful you look, and wanting to know about your diet and lifestyle. Imagine feeling hopeful, in control of your body and genuinely grateful when you go to sleep at night. Imagine not needing to spend a penny on prescription drugs. If you can, imagine, also, feeling so vibrantly healthy that you only visit your doctor once a year or so to get an annual checkup. And imagine your doctor's surprise and delight when you show up feeling and looking younger than your previous visit. It is music to the ear to hear the doctor say that you are in superior health and have the physiology of someone twenty years your junior, and the doctor wants to learn from *you* what you're doing to be so healthy.

With knowledge and determination, willingness and courage, you can make being out-of-shape and unhealthy a thing of the past. My goal is to offer you a reader-friendly book that provides a practicable roadmap, but it's up to you to make the healthy choices. The beauty of this Choose to Thrive program is that all the things that I recommend in this book that help increase energy, boost immunity, accelerate fat loss, reshape your physique, prevent disease and heal your body, also have the added bonus of helping to increase self-esteem and confidence, make you feel better and look younger and bring you more peace and balance.

You may find that I suggest things that are entirely new to you, such as meditation, visualization, solitude or spending time in nature. Maybe some of the foods, exercises or a new way of living are different from your present lifestyle. Don't just take my word for it: check things out. Notice how you feel when you eat more raw foods—such as fresh, organic fruits and vegetables—drink more water, get more sleep or enjoy a few quotidian minutes of peaceful solitude. You have all the answers within you. Always consult your inner guidance on every decision and choice in your life. The healthier you get, the more in-tune you will be with your innate guidance. Deep within our hearts, each of us knows the truth. But remember that active participation is important in reading this book. It's not what we read that makes a difference in our life; it's how we apply and experience the material that is of real value.

Like you, I have a myriad of things I want to accomplish in this life and I have no interest in being slowed down in any way by health issues. You owe it to yourself to choose being healthy and fit because no one is going to do it for you. You must make vibrant health on all levels—physically, mentally, emotionally and spiritually—your top priority. Don't give up. Don't ever give up! You can do anything to which you set your mind. Move in the direction of your dreams. I believe in you and your ability to be your best, and I salute your great adventure.

The lowest ebb is the turn of the tide.
— LONGFELLOW

My mission in life is not merely to survive, but to thrive; and to do so with some passion, compassion, humor and style. Each day I want to find people and things to celebrate, move in the direction of my dreams, appreciate resplendent nature all around me and open myself more fully to God's Love and Light and this miracle called life.
— SUSAN SMITH JONES

Introduction

Your life is really part of an unfolding plan,
a charted voyage, an exquisitely executed work of art.
—THOMAS KINKADE

If one advances confidently in the direction of his
dreams, and endeavors to live the life which he has
imagined, he will meet with a success unexpected
in common hours. . . .
If you have built castles in the air, your work
need not be lost; that is where they should be.
Now put foundations under them.
—HENRY DAVID THOREAU

STRESS IS A MAJOR PROBLEM IN MODERN LIFE. Technological advances have increased the pressure to keep busy, even during leisure hours. We talk on the telephone and text while we drive, watch television while we read, conduct business while we listen to the radio.

We are continually overstimulated, receiving more information from television, computers, radio and satellites than our ancestors of several generations ago ever could have imagined! This year alone you will probably make more appointments, meet more people and go more places than your grandparents did in their entire lives. All this manic rushing around creates a life filled with stress.

Given our current pace, we have little time to relax and cultivate relationships with our spouses, children, friends and nature. Is it any

wonder that stress-related diseases are now on the rise? Some studies even suggest that 80–90 percent of all doctor visits are for stress-related complaints. Stress-related illness is implicated in our rapidly escalating health care costs, and health problems attributed to job stress are estimated to cost U.S. businesses $150 billion every year.

I see unrelenting stress as a sickness of epidemic proportions—a "busyness" or "hurry" sickness. But you don't have to let it overwhelm you. You can *choose* to slow down and thrive—create a life of balance and joy. I'll address this throughout the pages of this book, but for now, let's see if you can find any of these signs of "hurry" sickness in your daily life.

1. Do you eat in a rush, eat while standing or walking or eat while driving?

2. Does your busy life prevent you from spending much time at home? And when you finally get home, are you too tired to do much beyond collapse and "veg out" in front of the television?

3. Do you routinely drive too fast, run yellow lights, constantly change lanes and jockey for position? Are you impatient with other drivers?

4. Do you talk fast, have problems communicating how you feel and lack the time to give emotional support to your family and friends?

5. Is your life so full of undone chores and responsibilities that relaxing has become almost impossible?

6. When you're not doing something productive, do you experience anxiety and guilt?

7. Have vacations become more trouble than they're worth?

8. Do you often feel tired and run-down, cry easily or have trouble sleeping?

9. Do you frequently get sick with colds or the flu, or find yourself experiencing one of the many prevalent diseases of Western society?

10. Do you make everyone and everything in your life more important than taking loving care of yourself?

What causes our need to rush and discount our own physical health needs? We can blame it on economics—and the need to make enough money to pay for our chosen lifestyles. We can blame it on the fact that everything's moving so fast, and we have to, too. But I believe the real cause is something deeper. By crowding our schedule with "more"—more socializing, more eating, more work, more activity, more appointments—we may be trying to fill the emptiness we feel inside ourselves.

When you constantly direct your attention and energies outward, it's easy to lose the sense of inner wonder, calmness, balance and beauty where true happiness, joy and peace originate. By slowing down and redirecting your energies inward, not only will you train your brain to relax, you will begin to reestablish the wholesome sense of self-worth necessary to positively change your life.

When you're under stress, your blood sugar levels can be affected. The stress response activates the adrenal glands' release of adrenal hormones. If the stress is continuous, the adrenal glands may not be able to generate enough adrenaline to raise blood sugar when you need it. Hypoglycemia, or abnormally low blood sugar levels, may result. Irritability is one of the symptoms of hypoglycemia.

Stress often produces anxiety, defined as "a state of being uneasy, apprehensive or worried about what may happen." According to the National Institute of Mental Health, anxiety disorders affect more than 20 million people in the United States.

How do you know when stress is getting the best of you? According to the latest edition of the *American Medical Association Family Medical*  *Guide,* physical symptoms of stress include headache, heart disease (two symptoms are atherosclerosis and high blood pressure), insomnia, absence of periods in women, impotence or premature ejaculation in men, digestive tract disturbances (such as ulcerative colitis, irritable bowel syndrome, gastritis, peptic and duodenal ulcers), back pain, frequent colds, shallow breathing, racing heart, herpes virus breakouts, slow wound healing and tight neck and shoulders.

Behavioral symptoms include an increase in smoking, an increase in alcohol consumption, grinding teeth, compulsive eating, an inability to get things done and bossiness. Emotional symptoms of stress include edginess, loneliness, nervousness, crying and a sense of powerlessness. Cognitive symptoms include forgetfulness, inability to make decisions, trouble thinking clearly, thoughts of escape, incessant worrying and lack of creativity.

You may not be able to change your boss's tendency to favor weekend workdays or control the bumper-to-bumper traffic to and from work, but you do have access to some powerful stress-busting tools. The simple fact that you are perusing this book tells me that you may be feeling out of balance and stressed out in one or several areas of your life. As a holistic lifestyle coach and counselor for more than 35 years, I've worked with thousands of people around the world. I offer my clients simple, yet essential, choices to bring purpose, harmony and health back into their lives. Stress may be a fact of modern life, but you don't have to let it become your way of life. You can become the master of your life, create a lifestyle of vitality and joy and keep noisome stress to a minimum. The path to contentment is in choosing to have your life in balance.

For easy reference, I've divided this book into four parts. In Part 1, we'll look at the physiology of stress, how it affects you and ways to live with balance and equanimity. In Part 2, we'll explore ways to fill your life with youthful vitality and experience true aliveness... no matter your age. In Part 3, I navigate through the best lifestyle practices to enrich your life. In Part 4, you'll learn about how to fill your days with prosperity and create the life of your dreams.

I encourage you to read the book through once in its entirety and then read it a second time more slowly and see which of the tips you can adopt in your life right away. Remember, it's not what you read that makes the difference. It's what you assimilate and put into practice in your life. And it's simply a matter of choice. Choose to create your best life, and start to live with balance and joy today!

Every beauty which is seen here below by personas of perception resembles more than anything else that celestial source from which we all come.
—MICHELANGELO

PART 1

Fill Your Life with Balance & Equanimity

*Take the complications, rules, shoulds,
musts, have tos, and so on out of your life. By
uncomplicating your life and removing the trivial
pursuits that occupy so much of it, you open a
channel for the genius within you to emerge.*
—WAYNE W. DYER

A FEW YEARS AGO, I GAVE A TALK IN LOS ANGELES on "Stress-Less Living: The Power to Be Your Best," during which I shared the essential stress-buster choices you'll be reading about in Part 3 of this book. One of the points I emphasized was the importance of putting inspiration back into your life, because when you feel inspired, you feel purposeful and you feel empowered. I also addressed the fact that many people are experiencing a crisis of the spirit, feeling disconnected from their authentic selves—the spiritual self within each of us and its connection with God, who is the source of Love and, yes, is Love. I believe what we need is a revolution of the spirit, a renewal of the spirit, one that unfolds naturally when you begin taking loving care of yourself, choose a more balance lifestyle and honor the love of God that is within you.

After my presentation, I went into the ladies' room and found a woman crying. I recognized her. She had been sitting in the front row of the audience and had cried through much of my talk. Since I had no plans for the evening, I asked if she would like to join me for dinner. She was surprised by my unexpected invitation, but she smiled, wiped away a tear and nodded yes.

MELISSA'S STORY: COMMIT TO EXCELLENCE

Melissa's story was heartbreaking. Her husband had recently left her for a much younger woman. She was almost one hundred pounds overweight, had no job, was living temporarily with her sister and needed to find a new home for herself and her children. She was so depressed she was actually considering suicide. One morning, when she was feeling at her lowest, she took a walk and noticed a flyer for my talk in the window of a natural food store. Something inside her told her she had to attend—even though she had never attended a motivational talk before.

Melissa believed in the ideas I discussed but wasn't sure how to implement them in her life. She knew she was falling downhill, but she didn't know how to climb back up. She wanted more than anything to turn her life around—to find a job and a decent place for her children, to lose weight and get back into shape and to live a balanced life. After listening to her story, I asked her to consider the possibility that the universe was taking everything away from her so that she could and would, for the first time in her life, put *herself* first. Like most women, she was so accustomed to putting everyone else's needs before her own that she took no time for herself. She was learning the hard way that you can't run on empty forever. She was being forced to learn that she had to take loving care of herself first, before she could nurture, love and take care of others.

I told Melissa that if she were willing to make a real commitment to do whatever it took to live her highest vision, I would be happy to work with her. For the rest of that evening, I asked her to share with me her highest vision and to answer questions like: "If you couldn't fail and if you were living your best life—right now—what would that look like?" At the end of the evening, I gave her copies of all my books and audio programs and wrote out a walking and meditation/prayer program that she could start the very next morning.

Over the next month, I designed a nutrition program for Melissa that included cleaning out her refrigerator and cupboards and removing all the processed (and junk) foods that didn't align with her new vision of herself. I taught her how to shop for healthy foods and nutritional supplements, how to make fresh vegetable juices, and how to create meals that emphasized organic, raw, colorful whole foods. I also customized a cardio-weights-stretching routine for her she could do at home or at a gym. Lastly, I taught her how to visualize her goals and practice deep breathing and meditation.

Melissa's favorite stress release was aerobic dance, but she was always too tired to participate when she got home from the very strenuous part-time job she found. So we found a lunchtime class offered at a gym in an office building near where she was working. She took an aerobic dance class there 3-5 times a week. As I told Melissa, researchers found that a 60-minute aerobic dance class improved the mood of participants, particularly those who were feeling depressed (J Sports Med Phys Fitness 2001;41[4]). And according to the National Institutes of Health, regular exercise (even 20 minutes daily) benefits mental health by reducing stress and increasing confidence. Melissa's entire attitude about work changed for the better when she scheduled in her dance classes during her lunch break.

Melissa was an inspiration. Her dedication and commitment created miraculous results. Three weeks after getting her part-time job, she applied for and was hired for a full-time one at a florist shop.

Within four months she had saved enough money to move into a large, new apartment with her very happy children.

Today, Melissa is down to her ideal weight, works out regularly, frequents natural food stores and manages the florist shop. She now lives with a sense of freedom, control and power over her life. She learned, firsthand, that breakthroughs and miracles occur when you are willing to live a balanced life—one that minimizes stress and maximizes joy.

A few months after he divorced her, Melissa's ex-husband said he wanted to get back together again. But she knew it wouldn't be for her highest good and said no. Soon afterwards, she met a wonderful man who supports her positive vision and they are engaged to be married. Needless to say, Melissa is feeling empowered and divinely guided.

DYING TO SUCCEED

Arthur, the president of a major American corporation, came to see me for a consultation. He also was stressed out, but for different reasons than Melissa. He was impatient, aggressive and sometimes hostile. He was totally unaware of how to make the necessary choices to quell stress and support his well-being. He routinely put in six or seven long, pressure-packed days a week at the office or traveling on business. He always had to be first, always had to be right and always had to be busy with work to feel worthwhile. Playful behavior did not enter into his lifestyle.

As a fancier of rich foods and a popular high-fat diet, he put away vast quantities of cheese, ice cream, steak, butter, processed foods and cream sauces. He knew his food was loaded with cholesterol and saturated fat, but he loved it all the same. As he told me once, when it came to food he could resist anything but temptation. His exercise was shifting gears in one of his expensive sports cars.

Arthur was chronically exhausted, but he thought that if he just had more time to spend in his hot tub with a drink he could easily relax and "unwind." He had trouble sleeping at night, and experienced

frequent headaches and backaches. He also developed several colds and a few bouts of the flu each year, but he assumed that was normal, and usually continued to work when sick. It wasn't until he began to sink into a deep depression that his wife urged him to have a medical checkup—his first in more than five years.

The doctor's report came as a shock to Arthur. He was only forty-five years old, but he had high blood pressure and serious hardening of the arteries (a symptom of heart disease). He was told that if he didn't make some changes in his way of life immediately, he was headed for a heart attack within six months. He also was headed toward needing quadruple-bypass heart surgery.

As providence would have it, the day after receiving the doctor's report, a friend of Arthur's told him about my holistic health private retreats and gave him several of my books and audio programs. Arthur quickly sought me out.

During the months we worked together, Arthur became a great inspiration to me, partly because his transformation was so dramatic. I had never worked with anyone quite so stressed and desperate, or who led such an unhealthful life. Fortunately, we were able to direct Arthur's innate drive to succeed toward a wholesome goal. During our first visit he made an important personal choice—he chose to make a commitment to change his life and restore the health of his younger years.

On the glorious splendor of Your majesty
and on Your wonderful works,
I will meditate.

—PSALM 145:5

I immediately started Arthur off with meditation and mindfulness training. As I explained to him, according to a study featured in the *American Journal of Health Promotion* (July 2001), meditation can help people reduce the psychological and physical effects of high stress. In the study, the participants who underwent "mindfulness training" experienced an average 54 percent reduction in psychological distress after three months on the program. The group that did not receive the meditation training experienced no significant reduction in their stress. (You'll learn more about meditation in Part 3.) Arthur took to this meditation discipline like a butterfly to buddleia (that's a beautiful, colorful butterfly-attracting plant).

The other practice I prescribed for him was bodywork at least two times a week. He worked with me and a variety of bodywork practitioners, exploring massage, acupressure, shiatsu, aromatherapy, neuromuscular therapy and myofascial trigger point therapy so that he could determine what was of most help to him. All of these disciplines can help reduce tension, relieve headaches and backaches, improve sleep and bring relaxation, calm and balance back into your life. A skilled massage therapist can knead tensed muscles and help dissipate any stress you may be holding in.

Arthur purchased a *Transcend Infrared Sauna* and enjoyed this heat therapy a few times weekly. You'll find information on the healing power of sweating and taking infrared saunas in Part 3.

Today, Arthur and his entire family are the picture of health. Recently they all participated in a 10-K run, and the following day they left on a two-week health and fitness vacation.

As Arthur and Melissa learned, choosing to live a balanced life, one filled with vibrant health, means much more than just feeling fine. It includes a quality of life, and a joy and radiance, that turns each and every moment of every day into a celebration. It's about body, mind and spirit working as one—harmoniously. For almost all of us, being radiantly healthy is a matter of choice, because we can choose to eat and live in a way that promotes vibrant health and enlivens us on physical, emotional, mental and spiritual levels.

It's hard to celebrate life when you're totally stressed out or when you're burdened with aches and pains, lethargy, obesity, heart disease, cancer, arthritis and the other prevalent diseases and ailments of our society. In my decades of work as a holistic lifestyle coach, I have seen thousands of people markedly improve their health and enrich their lives through the simple lifestyle and behavior changes you'll learn about in Parts 2 and 3. Before we get there, I will first provide you with a simple overview of stress and how it affects your body.

THE PHYSIOLOGY OF STRESS

Stress can be defined as a "synergy of endocrinological impairments that creates a syndrome." Loosely translated, that means that stress comes about when the sum total of your hormonal reactions to real and perceived events begins to have a significant effect on you. All day long, day after day, events in your life are triggering hormonal reactions in your body. If these reactions start to overwhelm your body's capacity to deal with them (either because there are simply too many of them and/or they are too intense), it can put a burden on you physically. Medical experts now believe that this stress-induced burden is at the root of many degenerative disease processes. In other words, stress has a biological as well as an emotional effect on you and, over time, it can diminish your body's ability to fortify, protect, regenerate and heal itself.

Stress can affect your life in many different ways—physically, emotionally, mentally and spiritually. Stress can precipitate high blood pressure, heart problems, fatigue, muscle and joint pain, headache, backache, anxiety, irritability, insomnia, gastrointestinal distress and that ever-growing culprit, obesity. Although a certain amount of appropriate stress actually can be beneficial, high amounts of stress can be detrimental, making you vulnerable to illness.

Stress can be triggered by emotions such as anger, fear, worry, grief, depression or guilt. It can be the result of a physical trauma, such as those caused by injury, accident or surgery. Everyday pressures, like family squabbles, impossible bosses, unfaithful spouses, unruly teens or overdue bills also cause stress. Extreme changes in your sleep pattern, diet, exercise or even the climate in which you live can create stress. So can chronic illness, pain, allergies and inflammation. Too much work—in fact, too much of *anything*—also can create stress that can lead to depression.

Stanford neuroendocrinologist and stress researcher Robert Sapolsky, the author of *Why Zebras Don't Get Ulcers,* recognizes how closely stress and depression are tied together, especially in women. Study after study has found that women suffer from both stress and depression more often than men. "Now we can begin to see how closely the two are linked. After all, depression is the archetypal stress-related illness," says Sapolsky.

Both Melissa and Arthur were good examples of the connection between stress and depression. Lisa, another one of my clients, was another classic example. Depression made it difficult for her to get up in the morning and face each day.

Lisa was a hard-working single mother of two in her late thirties, on the verge of becoming a partner in a law firm. In addition to putting in long hours at her office, she had to commute ninety minutes each way in heavy traffic. When she finally arrived home for the evening, she was greeted by screaming rap music blasting from her teenage son's room. With no time to call her own, Lisa felt like she had an endless list of things to do that never got completed.

Although she tried to watch her diet and to squeeze in two to three hours a week on her home treadmill, she was gaining weight monthly. Even more alarming, Lisa hadn't had a period in over a year. She was too young to be entering menopause, although she confessed that she felt twenty years older than her actual age.

At our first session, Lisa spoke to me through uncontrollable tears. In addition to admitting that she was having a hard time just getting out of bed in the morning, she said that she had been feeling a crippling despair for years, ever since she discovered her husband's addictions to gambling and infidelity. Just a few months after her divorce, when Lisa thought she was beginning to get her life back together, her mother died of cancer. Three weeks after the funeral, her daughter was in a serious automobile accident. Although her friends and neighbors all applauded her outward strength and ability to rise above these challenges and tragedies, inside she felt like she was losing control of herself and her life.

As I listened to Lisa's story, it became clear that she was in the midst of a severe depression. I explained to her that the physiological root of depression is often the chronic, overwhelming floods of hormones that release during times of extreme stress. I also mentioned that depression can be viewed as a form of self-hatred as well as anger with no place to go. For Lisa, and millions of people like her, finding ways to relieve stress would make the difference between waking refreshed—and bounding out of bed ready to face the day, or waking in a fog of depression—wanting to stay in bed and hiding under a dark blanket of despair.

When you fight rush-hour traffic or face a wall of rap music at the end of a demanding day, your brain, with the best of intentions, sounds an alarm. Your heart rate accelerates, your blood sugar soars, and an army of endorphins marches out to dull potential pain. A wave of neurotransmitters—serotonin among them—spreads the alarm from cell to cell throughout your nervous system. The hypothalamus also gets in on the act, releasing a hormone called CRH that signals for the release of other hormones. Meanwhile, the adrenal glands atop the kidneys send out the stress hormones adrenaline, DHEA and cortisol, also known as steroid hormones.

These substances are usually body-friendly and serve to protect us by increasing our alertness and strength to help us do what needs to be done. The problem comes when the stress is prolonged and the chemicals' normal routes change—serotonin tends to hasten away too quickly; DHEA can make itself scarce; cortisol can overstay its welcome.

CORTISOL'S ROLE IN STRESS & HORMONE BALANCE

Produced by the adrenal glands and commonly known as the "stress hormone," cortisol helps the body cope with all types of stress, from infection to fright, from a major job change or move to a new home, from a wedding to a divorce and from birth to death. Whether you are facing an emergency, an accident, a confrontation or just doing your job or getting some exercise, cortisol is there to get you up and going, to help get you through the day.

Cortisol helps determine how the proteins, carbohydrates and fats from your diet are utilized. For example, cortisol influences the breakdown of carbohydrates into glucose so the body can use them for energy. Cortisol also influences the breakdown of protein into amino acids. Amino acids are the building blocks of protein, and they are also the building blocks of the immune system, blood vessels, muscles and other tissues. Thus, the immune system, blood vessels and muscles all rely on cortisol for strength and proper function. Cortisol prevents the loss of too much sodium from the body and helps maintain blood pressure as well. It also helps to suppress reactions such as pain, allergic reactions and inflammation.

Perhaps most interesting of all, cortisol helps the body protect itself from itself. For example, during a strenuous workout, the body

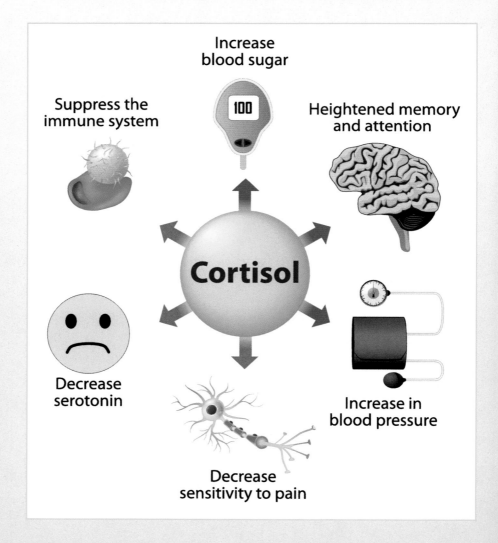

breaks down fat and muscle tissue to produce energy. In order to prevent the immune system from recognizing all of these tissue molecules as foreign invaders, the body produces more cortisol and gently suppresses the immune response so that the body does not go on red alert when it doesn't have to.

The cortisol that can flood your system to assist you in emergencies helps to provide your body with the nutrients you need to cope with stress. That's why it's known as the stress hormone. Typically, once you have managed the stressful circumstances, the brain shuts off the production of cortisol, your physical reactions subside and soon you are back to normal.

But there is another side of the cortisol story. If the brain perceives that stress is ongoing or chronic, it can override the signal to shut off cortisol production. Under those circumstances, cortisol production will stay elevated as long as the brain thinks the body needs it to cope with what it is experiencing. So, as important and necessary as cortisol is, you can have too much of it. If too much cortisol stays in the body for too long, a damaging cycle can begin that can lead to blood sugar problems, fat accumulation, compromised immune function, exhaustion, bone loss, even heart disease. If, like Lisa, you experience one major stress after another—and if you haven't created ways to reduce and release that stress—it can have a detrimental effect on your health.

Just like everything in nature, the body is in a continuous state of regeneration. It is constantly building itself up, tearing itself down and rebuilding itself all over again. Cortisol levels go up to provide the body with energy, but it breaks down tissue in order to do this. Once the job is done, the body has to rebuild and recuperate. That is when DHEA comes into play to help the body recuperate and get back to normal. DHEA and cortisol work together under normal conditions to handle stress.

Think back to the last time you felt a big rush of adrenaline. I felt it recently when I was invited to appear on a popular national television talk show. We experience these adrenaline rushes when we react to something that excites us, frightens us, surprises us or makes us angry. An adrenaline rush is the first in a chain reaction of hormonal events. It is the signal that sets in motion the release of cortisol and DHEA, which are the hormones that help us to take action, to get a job done and even to get our point across.

However, if you are always "under the gun"—which can mean anything from a continual struggle to make financial ends meet to traveling all the time because you are at the peak of your success in your career—then you constantly have stress hormones flooding into your bloodstream. When this happens, your adrenal glands can become overworked and exhausted. Over time, this excess wear and tear on them can be very serious, creating major disease. Given how most people live these days, it's no wonder that 80-90 percent of diseases are stress-related.

What endocrinologists have learned from studying women like Lisa, who are depressed or experiencing extended periods of stress, is that continually elevated levels of cortisol can prevent them from ovulating. The cessation of regular ovulation means that not enough estrogen and progesterone are being produced. Low estrogen levels can increase the activity of the bone-metabolizing osteoclasts. To further complicate things, the cortisol that provides the extra calcium needed in a fight-or-flight situation also stimulates the bone-metabolizing osteoclasts. Left unchecked over a long period of time, high cortisol levels can cause the body to lose bone faster than it is able to replace it. Low levels of progesterone can lead to many serious problems, including weight gain, PMS symptoms, fluid retention, depression, low energy and libido, blood sugar and mineral imbalances and osteoporosis.

In a natural rhythm, the body produces much more cortisol in the morning than in the evening. This helps you to get up and get going, and also helps you to get through your day. At the end of the day, your cortisol level should be going down. One recent study demonstrated that when men come home from work, their cortisol levels go down. This is what is supposed to happen when you come home and wind down. However, the same study showed that the cortisol levels of women like Lisa who work outside the home and still have primary responsibility for taking care of their homes and families stay elevated in the evening. This is evidence that their bodies are responding to the stress of the "second shift." Women who have high cortisol and low DHEA levels can experience panic attacks and a strange feeling of being both anxious and exhausted at the same time.

CORTISOL, FOOD CRAVINGS & WEIGHT GAIN

Everyday pressures, recent surveys reveal, cause nine out of ten of us to look to food for comfort. In fact, almost 40 percent of Americans polled say that they always eat when they see food, and this survey didn't even factor in how this pattern is affected when we're under stress. But if you're one of those people who turn to food during stressful periods in your life, don't be hard on yourself. What at first may seem like bad eating habits, writes Pamela Peeke, MD, a former senior scientist at the National Institutes of Health and author of *Fight Fat After Forty*, are, in fact, "our body's natural reaction to stress. And strict dieting can actually make you more stressed out, and more prone to weight gain."

Peeke says that when you're wound up as tight as a spring, the brain sends out signals—in the form of hunger—to stockpile emergency fuel. But today, it's not because we're fleeing from tigers; it's our day-to-day stresses—struggling with overdue bills, unruly teens, inconsiderate neighbors, loud rap music, relationship challenges, illness in the family, terrorist threats, unending traffic and other environmental stimulation. So we're left full of nervous tension, "which we often soothe by chewing," says Dr. Peeke. And that emergency fuel we stockpiled? It stays stockpiled—as fat, of course.

What's more, to create instant energy, the body drains its nutritional reserves. Under extreme stress, we need extra good quality protein (as you find in green vegetables and their fresh juices and other superior plant-based sources). What if we haven't eaten that much? The body uses its own protein-rich tissues—namely muscle. In my books *The Curative Kitchen & Lifestyle* and *Invest in Yourself with Exercise*, you can read more about how important lean muscle tissue is to keeping metabolism revved, increasing fat-burning enzymes and burning more calories, even when sleeping. And for every pound of muscle destroyed through stress, our metabolism drops, burning approximately 50 fewer calories a day.

Do you ever wonder why some people appear to thrive on stress, while others suffer ill health? New studies suggest that it may not be the stress that lowers immunity, but whether you feel a sense of control over it. In one Dutch study, scientists compared two groups of men taking a math test under a barrage of noise. Those who could adjust the noise level had little change in immune function, while those who couldn't experienced a drop in immune-cell production. In many cases, feeling in control has more to do with your attitude than your situation. And as you'll see in the tips that follow, choosing to be positive and optimistic, and reminding yourself that you're doing the best you can, will do wonders toward keeping the negative repercussions of stress at bay.

So what can we do to break the negative stress cycle? Although stress can overwhelm us at times, we can choose to take the steps necessary to keep it manageable. First, we need to understand what it means to live a balanced, joyful life. Next, we need to put that understanding into practice. Vibrant health and peace of mind (the opposite of stress) go hand in hand—you can't reach your potential for physical health without being mentally fit as well. Making choices that integrate and heal the body, mind and spirit is what thriving and living with balance (experiencing more joy and less stress) is all about.

Everything can be taken from a man but
one thing; the last of human freedoms—
to choose one's attitude in any given set of
circumstances, to choose one's own way.

—Victor Frankl

HUMOR  TIME

Between the parts of this book, I have created four Humor Time breaks with some funny jokes or phrases about diet, foods, aging and health in general. Everybody loves to laugh. In fact, did you know that laughter is very good for you? It was Norman Cousin who said: "Laughter is a form of internal jogging." Humor and laughter have both been found to be important components of healing. It's been reported that laughter aids digestion, stimulates the heart, strengthens muscles, activates the brain's creative function and keeps you alert. Laughter also helps you to keep things in better perspective. So make up your mind to laugh and to be happy. When you laugh at yourself, you take yourself far less seriously. "Angels fly because they take themselves lightly," says an old Scottish proverb. Isn't that wonderful?

I simply love to laugh and am known to be a practical joker! My mother June called laughter "the body's elixir" or natural rejuvenator. It is an essential ingredient to daily living and something I use to fuel my spirituality. Because of my positive, easygoing, "lighten up" approach to life, I have acquired the nickname "Sunny" because I am always reminding others to not take life so seriously.

So let's start with this first batch of jokes and funny phrases. If there's no name given to the joke, quote or phrase—that is because the author is unknown.

There are four basic food groups: milk chocolate,
dark chocolate, white chocolate, and chocolate truffles.

Strength is the capacity to break a chocolate
bar into four pieces with your bare hands—
and then eat just one of the pieces.
—Judith Viorst

Part of the secret of a success in life is to eat what you like and let the food fight it out inside.

—Mark Twain

What kind of food should you eat to increase your vision? —Seafood

Why did the raisin go to the dance with the prune? —Because he couldn't get a date.

What kind of lettuce was served on the Titanic? —Iceberg

What did the teddy bear say when he was offered dessert? —No thanks, I'm stuffed!

What do cats call mice on skateboards? —Meals on wheels.

I am not gaining weight—I'm retaining food.

Put 'eat chocolate' at the top of your list of things to do today. That way, at least you'll get one thing done.

My doctor told me to stop having intimate dinners for four—unless there are three other people.

—Orson Welles

The secret of staying young is to live honestly, eat slowly, and lie about your age.

—Lucille Ball

The only way to keep your health is to eat what you don't want, drink what you don't like, and do what you'd rather not.

—Mark Twain

PART 2

Nurture Your Life with Vitality & Experience Aliveness

OUR LIVES ARE MADE UP OF MILLIONS OF CHOICES. Moment to moment, we are always choosing. What we are consists of the sum of our choices: what we think, what we imagine, how we react, what we eat, what we say, what we feel and what we expect. It's time to take back the responsibility for our own lives and start using the power that is ours to create what we want—a healthy, fit body and a fulfilling, joyful and peaceful life.

Let's explore more closely the importance of our day-to-day food (and other lifestyle) choices and the need to reprogram and retrain our senses to release self-limiting beliefs and habits. Your primary goal on what I refer to as my "Experience Aliveness" program is to get to the point where you are eating a reasonable amount of the highest quality foods and adopting positive, health-promoting lifestyle habits. More than 2,400 years ago, Pythagoras said, "Choose what is best; habit will soon render it agreeable and easy."

Although it's important to choose healthy foods, don't become a fanatic about what you eat. It's what you choose to eat on a daily basis that makes the difference, not the occasional lapse. Worrying about every little piece of food that goes into your mouth is far more harmful in the long run than infrequent splurges.

Learn to think in terms of *whole foods*. It's when you begin cutting, cooking and processing foods that your system gets into trouble. Whenever you are able, eat your foods whole, just the way nature made them, complete with vitamins, minerals, enzymes, amino acids, natural sugars, fibers and water, in the right proportions for efficient use by your body. Fresh organic fruits and vegetables, legumes, nuts and seeds and sprouts carefully selected and prepared to suit your particular needs and desires are ideal foods for the vibrantly alive body. (Please refer to my book *Body Temple Vitality* on how to become a kitchen gardener—the ABCs of growing fresh, delicious, healthy sprouts at home in a few days and in three minutes of your time daily.)

You may feel that it's too difficult to switch all at once to a new nutritional, natural-foods program. That's a common reaction and that's OK. You can break in gradually, if you wish, switching first to the foods that appeal to you the most and gradually adding the others. Or perhaps, choose to eat fresh fruit for breakfast, a colorful salad for lunch with lots of leafy greens and vegetables, with another salad for dinner with some cooked plant-based food in the evening such as a bowl of soup and steamed vegetables. It may take a few weeks for your digestive system to become accustomed to handling these new whole, high-fiber, living foods.

MIND POWER—USE IT TO YOUR ADVANTAGE

Your mind may have some negative programming about your eating habits that will trip you up if you aren't careful. The mind will always choose immediate gratification over long-term satisfaction. The mind doesn't care if you achieve your long-term goal for a fit, lean, healthy body. The mind wants you to feel good right now. It's important to realize that the mind isn't necessarily your friend. You must sometimes detach from it to achieve your long-term goals.

Whether for food or something else, the difficulty in resisting sensory desire comes from the force of conditioning. Every time we are negatively conditioned, we lose a little of our freedom and our capacity to choose. So begin by becoming aware of what you are eating. Eating at the table, at mealtimes and only when you are hungry, help because you can more fully focus your attention on your food. When our attention is divided, we eat compulsively rather than from hunger. Automatic eating occurs frequently in front of the television set or at a movie theater, parties or sports events.

The entire process of eating needs to be given your full attention to get the maximum benefits. Be conscious of the hunger you feel before you eat, how the food looks and smells as you prepare it, serve it and eat it; how the table setting looks; how the food tastes; the texture of the food; your chewing; your breathing; and how you feel while you are eating. Finally, after all this, be aware of and grateful for the feelings of lightness and high energy derived from the meal and the easy elimination of the food after it's digested. It's embracing this attitude about meals that enables you to appreciate simple, wholesome foods and to eat less, feeling completely satisfied. Paying attention helps to develop the capacity to enjoy the simplest foods and to be truly healthy.

Stop eating just before you feel really full. In this way you are reprogramming your subconscious and are taking control rather than letting your habits control you. Stopping short of satiety helps you savor your food and helps you to be free and in charge of your choices.

Begin the retraining of your senses by eliminating things that injure the body. None of us would drive into a service station and fill the gas tank with oil. For the car to run efficiently, we must use a particular type of gas, lubricant, coolant and so on. Yet, when it comes to our bodies, we are often not so careful. We put in all kinds of things that nutritionists, and plain common sense, tell us impair the body's smooth functioning, just because they taste pleasant. We need to reestablish that the determinant of what we eat should be our body's needs, not merely the appeal of the senses. I have found that meditating/praying for a few seconds or minutes before each meal is a powerful tool that fosters choosing foods that promote health and harmony.

Ralph Waldo Emerson said, "Health is our greatest wealth." How true that is! It does seem that our taste buds change and adapt when we alter our eating habits and the whole grain granola that tasted heavy and grainy a few months ago may taste chewy and flavorful this month. Feeling better and looking marvelous will soon compensate for the loss of dubious taste thrills of the past, such as fried chicken, white bread, ice cream, candy and potato chips. You'll find yourself looking forward to more healthful pleasures—the taste of ripe papaya, luscious strawberries, blueberries, ripe pineapple, sweet juicy grapes, a crisp garden salad, a sprouted veggie burger on whole grain bread, and a delicious melt-in-your-mouth fresh fruit "ice cream" dessert.

DANIELLA'S STORY:
CHANGE YOUR DIET, CHANGE YOUR LIFE

Daniella is a great example of how changing our diet and adding more living, whole foods can not only assist with weight loss, but also improve every aspect of family life and self-esteem. Married, with three children ages five, eight and twelve, Daniella initially came to me for motivation and help in losing some fat, toning up her body and increasing her energy. As a first step, I asked her to keep a 14-day food diary and record exactly what and when she ate. Like all my new clients, she was instructed not to eat differently simply because I would be looking at the list; she had to be honest and write down everything, because there's no other way to make a true evaluation.

When I received her food diary, it was quite apparent why she had gained almost 30 pounds in 18 months and always felt enervated. Her diet was about 60 percent fat, the carbohydrates she consumed were almost all refined, she usually skipped breakfast because she was too busy getting the kids ready for school, and she always ate late at night. Her diary came straight out of my "encyclopedia of deleterious habits!" She rarely included raw foods in her diet, or her family's, explaining that it took too long to chew the food and she didn't have time. Daniella also noted that her kids disliked raw foods,  so only on rare occasions did she have a few fruits and vegetables in the house. (Her youngest child loved my colorful 2-in-1 nutrition book for children ages 1–8 titled *Vegetable Soup/The Fruit Bowl,* co-authored with Dianne Warren, and, as a result of reading it often, she started eating—and even enjoying—healthier foods. For more information on this book or to purchase, please visit: **SusanSmithJones.com**.)

As I inquired more about her family life, routines, eating habits and so on, I learned that all her children were on the heavy side. The oldest girl was starting to be ridiculed in school because of her size. Not surprisingly, Daniella told me that her husband also needed to lose about 50 pounds. His blood pressure, cholesterol and triglycerides were much too high and his doctor had suggested that he go on a diet. I told Daniella that no diet was necessary. Her family needed a health makeover, and I assured her that she had come to the right person for guidance.

My initial evaluation of how they ate and lived led me to suggest something very out of the ordinary. Knowing that they had a very large house with a guest room next to the kitchen, I asked if I could stay with them from Thursday through Saturday night. I wanted to experience their lifestyle as a family, to see how they lived at home, when and what they ate and how they spent their time when not eating, in order to coach them in a healthier way of living. Yes, I brought most of my own food, and I simply observed like a butterfly on the wall (I like butterflies better than flies) and took lots of notes. I had Daniella's permission, when they were out of the house, to look through their pantry and refrigerator and all their kitchen cupboards. Sure enough, I found hardly any fresh, whole foods.

At mealtime, everyone salted the food before tasting it, and their dining table was never without canned sodas or processed fruit juices, butter, sour cream and mounds of cheese. All five of them ate their meals quickly, without much conversation and without putting the utensils down between bites. Much overeating may be unintentional, since many popular foods contain hidden sugar and oils put there to stimulate the taste buds, and this was definitely the case with Daniella's family.

With Daniella's consent, I made a clean sweep of her kitchen. The rest of her family went along, although they were far from enthusiastic. I removed all refined carbohydrates, including pasta, white rice, low-fiber cereals, pancake and cookie mixes, white breads and bagels, and give them to a homeless shelter. I replaced these with high-fiber breads and whole grains. I also rid their kitchen of margarine, mayonnaise and vegetable shortenings and oils. Next, I gave away all the whole milk and cheese products. Those high-fat, calorie-loaded cheese slices provide between 80 and 140 calories per one-ounce slice, depending on the fat content. I replaced the whole milk with raw nut and seed milks; it turned out that they all loved the vanilla-flavor almond beverage the best after about two weeks of adapting to the new taste.

I took the entire family to the nearest health food store, showed them all the healthy alternatives such as veggie burgers and whole-grain

pastas and, to the amazement of all of them, let them experience the produce section of the store. They were enthralled by all the colors and varieties of fruits and vegetables, many of which they had never seen before. We started with some of the most familiar—organic apples, oranges, pears, grapes, bananas and strawberries.

In place of sodas and other canned drinks, I taught them how to make their own juice. The kids loved juicing and actually wanted to take it over as their daily job. Of course, I encouraged them to start drinking more water. Daniella's husband confessed to me secretly that he couldn't remember having more than about six glasses of water weekly. When I told him that I drink half of my body weight in ounces of purified, alkaline water every day, he almost collapsed in shock.

Yes, it took about one month for the family to adjust their taste buds to the new flavors, textures and colors of their foods. They basically switched from a white and beige diet to a banquet of rainbow colors. Almost half of their diet was now raw foods, with an abundance of fresh fruits and vegetables. When you fill up on these salubrious foods, you nourish your body and actually lose much of your desire for junk or other processed foods.

After three months, it was time to introduce them to the benefits of consuming more raw foods and also showed them several simple raw-food recipes they could enjoy often. They were eager to move in that direction. After several un-cooking lessons, Daniella found it wasn't so hard to create healthier meals. As a result of eating more fiber and more nutritious foods, the family all lost weight, had more energy and balanced moods and a greater sense of well-being that resulted in more positive attitudes all around. I encouraged them all to be more active instead of hanging out in front of televisions or computers most nights and weekends, and their higher activity resulted in sounder sleep for everyone. Daniella's oldest daughter lost weight and joined an after-school sports team, which ended the ridicule and helped her self-esteem soar.

It's truly remarkable how making a few basic changes in one's diet can profoundly affect every area of life. The change this family had the hardest time with initially, but which ultimately turned out to be the most fun, was the one day each week of raw food. Remember, when I first met them, about 95% of their diet was all cooked foods. So, I suggested they not pick a weekend day but rather a Tuesday, Wednesday or Thursday. They selected Thursday and from morning through evening ate only living foods—lots of fruits and vegetables, salads and a variety of other fun foods, including nut butters, sprouts, sauces, soups—even cookies and other desserts. The family came to appreciate Daniella's gift for experimenting and creating new raw-food meals. A few weeks into their new health regimen, they started having friends over for meals to sample their delicious "health nut food!"

As I mentioned above, even though you may not be eager to overhaul your entire food program, at least start by adding more raw enzyme-rich organic fruits and vegetables to your diet. I recommend the following program to my clients and friends. Make at least 60 percent of your diet raw each and every day. On Mondays, eat raw foods all day until dinner, and on Thursdays, raw foods all day *including* dinner. This simple program will assist you to bring more living foods into your diet by spacing them out over the week. You'll feel lighter and more energetic immediately, simply from eating more uncooked foods.

10 SIMPLE STEPS FOR SUCCESS WHEN MAKING A FRESH START

Here are some salutary guidelines I use with my clients and friends that can make a profound difference and foster success with your whole-food choices and new aliveness lifestyle.

1 Start strong. Pick a day to begin your new program and make the start date a special date. If you're near the end of the month, wait until the beginning of the next month or the beginning of the next week. I sometimes pick the new moon or the first day of a new season or the beginning of a month. Just as the first 40 minutes of each day set the tone for the day, so we want to make them relaxed, peaceful and positive, the first day of your new program sets the tone for the next few months.

The days before your program starts, mentally, emotionally and spiritually prepare. Do whatever you need to do to clean out your kitchen of unhealthy products, get your workout clothes and shoes in order and create a monthly calendar you can place on your refrigerator door where each day you will list your physical activities and all the other ways you've loved yourself. For example, you might write that you walked for 30 minutes, devoted 15 minutes to prayer and meditation, ate 3 pieces of fresh fruit and put a rejuvenation mask on your face before going to bed. Seeing the squares filled in provides you with a mirror of how well you're taking care of yourself and brings a feeling of empowerment.

2 Eat your morning meal. Make sure that you start the day with a healthy, whole-foods breakfast. Embracing each day with a strong, positive start makes it easier to make healthier choices throughout the day and also stokes your metabolism. People who eat a healthy breakfast generally feel less hungry throughout the day. Learn how to make delicious green smoothies that even kids love. I often include blueberries, fresh if in season or frozen other times of the year. It's easy to hide the baby leaf spinach and kale in this purple smoothie. (Refer to my website, **SusanSmithJones.com**, for recipes.)

3 Curb your appetite. Drink a large glass of purified, alkaline water (refer to pages 75–80) about 15–20 minutes before a meal. Water does wonders for detoxifying and rejuvenating your body and helps to prevent overeating by making you feel full. Also, the extra fiber that you'll be eating in your whole-foods diet will fill you up and leave you feeling satisfied.

4 Eat smaller meals more frequently. The more whole foods that you eat, the healthier you will be, the more energy you will have and the easier it will be to achieve your ideal weight. If you want to see changes in your body shape fast, and you desire to accelerate fat loss, rather than eating 1–3 large meals daily, choose to eat 5–6 smaller meals throughout the day. Grazing stokes your metabolism. As you adopt a whole-foods diet, you'll see your extra weight melt away easily and effortlessly. Keep in mind, also, that for the best, most restorative sleep, strive not to eat right before bedtime, unless it's something that's light and easy to digest such as a piece of fresh, juicy fruit, some freshly made green juice or a light green smoothie.

5 Feel your hunger. Try to eat your meals and snack when you're hungry, not just because the clock says it's time, or when you're bored or depressed or tired or anything but hungry. Remember, we want to eat to live, not live to eat.

6 Go light. When your tummy really wants food and you don't have much time, opt for low-calorie bites that are quick and nourishing, such as carrot and celery sticks or other fresh vegetables or fresh fruit. If you crave more substance, add a few raw seeds or nuts, but no more than one ounce at a time if you have more than ten pounds to lose.

7 **Eat what you like.** There are so many delicious healthy whole foods to choose from, there's simply no reason to eat foods you don't like. And nothing makes a food program more difficult than forcing yourself to eat foods you don't care for. So make wise, healthy choices from the foods you really like.

8 **Slow down.** Eat slowly enough to give your body time to release the enzymes that tell your brain when you've had all you need. Inhaling food instead of eating consciously and deliberately causes indigestion and gas. Also, chew your foods well. Half of digestion takes place in your mouth.

9 **Don't give up.** Falling off your health program once or twice does not mean the effort is hopeless. Simply acknowledge that you didn't eat wisely and get back on the program. To help you get back on track, to motivate you to live closer to Nature and to learn about some sure-fire Natural Home Remedies you can use for yourself and your family, please visit my website. While there, be sure to sign up for my free monthly *Healthy Living Newsletters* that the general public never sees; they are exclusive for my subscribers only—my extended family.

10 **Reward yourself.** Treat yourself with a massage, a movie, a new piece of clothing, a new book, a visit to a museum, art show or resplendent flower garden or, or a delicious meal at your favorite restaurant (that offers healthy meals) for each week that you maintain your health program, achieve goals or maintain weight. Also, whenever possible, attend healthy living and whole-food conferences such as the ones offered by the National Health Association. I've been a member of the NHA for over 40 years and enjoy their informative, quarterly magazine *Health Science*. For more information, or to become a member, visit HealthScience.org. Their annual conferences are a great way to build your motivation and spend time with like-mind, uplifting people.

Two roads diverged in a wood, and I—
I took the one least traveled by,
and that has made all the difference.

—ROBERT FROST

There is a profound benefit to hitting the pause button
on your life every so often to create mini-respites,
enabling you to connect with your inner silence and
power—the love and light of God within you.

—SUSAN SMITH JONES

THE 21 SALUBRIOUS SUPERFOODS

Refer to my book *The Curative Kitchen & Lifestyle* for detailed information on these 21 superfoods. Of course, there are many others, but these are a good place to start.

Avocado	Garlic & Onions
Beans	Kale
Beets	Kiwi
Blueberries	Nuts—Almonds & Walnuts
Broccoli	Peppers—Chilies & Red Bell
Cantaloupe	Pomegranate
Carrots & Parsnips	Sea Vegetables
Citrus—Grapefruit, Lemon & Orange	Spices—Cinnamon & Ginger
Cucumber	Spinach
Flaxseed	Strawberries
	Sunflower Seeds & Sprouts

HUMOR  TIME

Everything you see I owe to spaghetti.
—Sophia Loren

This recipe is certainly silly. It says to separate two eggs, but it doesn't say how far to separate them.
—Gracie Allen

My mother's menu consisted of two choices: Take it or leave it.
—Buddy Hackett

I'm in shape.
Unfortunately, it's the wrong one.

Number one rule of dieting:
If it tastes good, spit it out.

A good run is like a cup of coffee... I'm much nicer after I've had one.

Here's my best advice if you are starting a jogging program. Start slow, then taper off.
—Susan Smith Jones

Age is an issue of mind over matter.
If you don't mind, it doesn't matter.
—Mark Twain

You know you're getting old when the
candles cost more than the cake.

—BOB HOPE

Children are a great comfort in your old age,
and they help you reach it faster, too.

—LIONEL KAUFFMAN

I didn't get old on purpose, it just happened.
If you're lucky, it could happen to you.

—ANDY ROONEY

Some days you eat salads and go to the gym.
Some days you eat cupcakes and refuse to
put on pants. It's called balance.

Your stomach shouldn't be a waist basket.

I have this theory that chocolate slows
down the aging process... It may not be
true, but do I dare take the chance?

PART 3

Honor Your Life with 13 Enriching Lifestyle Choices

Everyone is born a genius,
but the process of living de-geniuses them.
—BUCKMINSTER FULLER

EACH OF US FACES TREMENDOUS CHALLENGES every day. As we get up each morning, we may face myriad stressors—getting the kids off to school, driving in bumper-to-bumper traffic, presenting a career-making (or career-breaking) report to the boss, balancing the household budget and so much more. It can seem like there is not enough time in the day to accomplish all you need to do. These are just some of the ways everyday life can get us down. If poorly managed, these challenges can lead to many forms of stress, depression and anxiety.

Stress is a fact of life, but you can choose not to make it a way of life for you. By incorporating most or all of the tips below, you will experience more joy and less stress; you will start thriving in your life. You will be well on your way to creating a healthy, happy, peaceful, fulfilling and soul-satisfying life. Not only do these tips help assuage stress, they also help prevent and alleviate disease and depression, boost energy and restore youthful vitality.

Living a stress-free life is not a reasonable goal. The real goal is to learn to deal with stress actively and effectively. Although that's easier for some people than others, studies suggest that anyone can learn to cope better. But I don't want you to just cope; I want you to *thrive*—to be vibrantly healthy, joyful and balanced.

Here are 13 simple, yet essential, choices that I recommend and use with clients, friends and family members to bring more vitality and purpose into one's body and life. I have found them to be profoundly efficacious and practicable. Making a new life for yourself is simply a matter of choice.

So today, *choose to...*

1. CELEBRATE YOURSELF & CHAMPION HIGH SELF-ESTEEM

Have you ever stopped to think about how unique, special and marvelous you are? No one else in the world, now or in the past or in the future, is exactly like you. Never, from amongst all the eighty billion humans who have walked this planet since the beginning of time, has there been anyone exactly like you. As I thought about this concept recently, I thought about the approximately 7.6 billion people living on our planet. Then I figured out how long it would take to count all these people if they passed by me single file, one every second.

Imagine this. A clock ticks out the seconds while you sit in a rocking chair on your front porch. Without taking time out to stretch your legs, eat your meals, or rest your eyes, count each person passing by. How many weeks or months do you think it would take to count the world's population, one per second? You would have to sit there continuously for about 200 years! *By that time you would probably be off your rocker!*

This calculation of the world's population is an amazing lesson in the miraculousness of life. Try to grasp the idea that for 200 years you would never find two people exactly alike. You would never find two whose experiences had been the same or whose fingerprints were alike, or who thought, believed, felt or talked alike.

And then to that, add the fact that you are the one special being created from one egg and one out of more than 500 million sperm that traveled an immense distance, overcame tremendous obstacles and won a fierce and challenging competition at the moment of your conception. *You are already a winner.* What's more, you are composed of a body, mind and spirit, and you already have everything you need to live up to your highest potential—to become master of your life. You are made in the image and likeness of God. I think that calls for a celebration. You are amazing in who you are and what you can do with your life.

Here's an uplifting quote from Shakespeare's *Hamlet* that I'd like you to memorize and remind yourself of often: "What a piece of work is a man! How noble in reason! How infinite in faculty! In form, and moving, how express and admirable! In action, how like an angel! In apprehension, how like a god! The beauty of the world! The paragon of animals!"

On a universal level, I believe the thing that people wrestle with most in their own lives is low self-esteem. That's why I'm making this the first tip and choice to consider and apply in your life. When you embrace high self-esteem and live from an empowered presence, you will be successful in all areas of your life. It's an inner change that needs to be made. Look at magazine ads, television commercials or makeover reality shows; either by innuendo or by outright declaration, they are almost all aimed at changing who we are, making us somehow better—smarter, more attractive, slimmer, richer and more secure. You can spend millions of dollars changing your physical features, but that will do little good until you change your attitude about yourself and cultivate a relationship with yourself that incorporates your very own divinity. When you do that, chances are you'll be happy with the physical body that God provided for you, and you will establish a salutary health and fitness program to keep your body temple in peak functioning order. (Refer to my book *Body Temple Vitality*.)

We must *choose* to be kind and loving toward ourselves—all the time. Self-image is crucial here. Being vibrantly healthy, living fully and celebrating life starts with celebrating ourselves. Whether we succeed or fail, enjoy our lives or struggle, depends largely on our self-image. In fact, numerous studies have concluded that the view we have of ourselves is the key to taking control of our lives. Develop a loving relationship, a warm friendship with yourself. Be your own best friend. Out of that friendship all your other relationships form. Stop being so critical, judgmental and unforgiving of yourself. When you are not feeling good about yourself, you feel separated from others and God. When you see yourself as a failure, you create a self-fulfilling prophecy. You attract to yourself that which you believe you deserve. Your negative thoughts and attitudes about yourself, whether they originated within yourself or from others, convince you of your inability to succeed. If you feel you don't deserve success, prosperity, an enjoyable life, happy relationships or joy and peace, you will settle for less than that to which you are entitled. When you feel unworthy, you cut yourself off from the fullness of life and create more stress. Put simply, *when you learn to love yourself and take loving care of yourself, love will come to you in the forms of happiness, health, success, prosperity, peace, joy and balance.*

Living in such a fast-paced world, constantly in a tizzy over one thing or another, conspires against inner peace. The intense pace and stress of our daily lives can very easily put our peace, joy, urbanity and health—not to mention our spiritual lives—at risk. It's easy to get caught up in the whirl of today's hectic lifestyle—especially if we've forgotten the truth of our potential. This leaves us less time for self-fulfillment. Deteriorating standards and values lead to low self-esteem and rob many of us of our dignity.

When we feel an inner emptiness, we are less inclined to make the difficult decisions of life and may be tempted to seek "easy" solutions to problems. This "quick fix" approach to life is understandable, since learning to live fully takes time and patience. But the fact is, we can, and must, slow things down if we ever hope to face our own large and small challenges with aplomb and equanimity, on terms that are our own, guided by our purest hearts. We can choose to experience aliveness and become masters of our lives, keeping in mind that this awakening is always an "inside job."

In the 1960s, Abraham Maslow wrote his famous book, *Toward a Psychology of Being,* which helped turn around the emphasis of psychology. Psychology was my undergraduate major at UCLA, and I was drawn to Maslow's work. Unlike most psychologists of his day, he chose to study high-functioning people—those living their highest potential—rather than people with problems. Maslow developed a psychology of being—not of striving, but arriving and thriving; not of trying to get someplace, but living fully. He found a common denominator among all his high-functioning subjects. They all had a vision and

were committed to it, believed they had the power to master life and were self-motivated and disciplined. Do you believe you have the power to master life? How committed, motivated and disciplined are you to follow your highest vision and purest heart's desire?

2. EXEMPLIFY COMMITMENT & PERSONAL SELF-DISCIPLINE

Breakthroughs and miracles occur when people are willing to live from their highest vision, commitment and discipline. A commitment is the honoring of a decision. When you're committed, you allow nothing to deter you from reaching your goal. You are disciplined even when you are not feeling motivated. Making a commitment is being willing to put all of your resources on the line and taking responsibility for the outcome.

Commitment—to a project, a relationship, a health and fitness program or a spiritual practice—can lend stability to the stressful, chaotic whirlwind of everyday life. Daily actions that reaffirm commitments bring a feeling of empowerment and increase self-esteem. *It's through our everyday behavior that we know what really counts.* Our commitment must be woven through all of life—our thoughts, our emotions, our words and our actions.

I know many people who say they are committed to being healthy, yet they continually let excuses get in the way. They say they'll have to wait until next Monday to exercise because they're just too busy now; they won't be able to eat nutritious food for the next two weeks because of birthdays, anniversaries and the church's bake sale coming up; or they're too stressed to make a major change right now. Commitment means that you get past your excuses and follow through on what you said you were going to do. Make your word count. Be responsible and accountable. How do you ever expect someone to make a commitment to you or think you will follow through on a commitment to them unless you first show a commitment to yourself and what you say? Commitment takes organization, follow-through and a big dose of mettle. If you are ready for commitment, you will be committed. In other words, you will arrange your personal circumstances so that your lifestyle, in every way, supports your commitment. You will do the things you need to do to order your life, eliminate the nonessentials and the superfluous, and consciously focus on what is important.

I know that many people wish they felt more committed, wish they had something really big to commit to. These people do not realize that *you can't be committed to anything if you aren't committed to yourself.* By really committing to yourself, by following through on your convictions and decisions and allowing nothing to stand in the way of your becoming the master of your life, you will quell stress, experience more balance and joy and gain tremendous power. But to be committed, you must choose to be disciplined. Discipline is a choice. If we are to live our highest potential, we must practice self-discipline in every aspect of our lives. The mountain of soul-achievement and fulfillment cannot be scaled by anyone faint of heart or by anyone who lacks control of body, mind and emotions.

Discipline, to me, means *the ability to carry out a resolution long after the mood and enthusiasm has left you.* It also means doing what you say you're going to do.

Discipline brings freedom, joy and balance to your life. A disciplined person is not at the whim or mercy of external circumstances but is in control of what he or she thinks, feels, says and does. An undisciplined person is lazy, undirected and usually unhappy. Mind discipline creates body discipline. And from a disciplined body comes an exhilarated mind.

We cannot very well discipline ourselves in the great things of life unless, and until, we have learned and accepted that discipline must begin with the small things. It's been my experience that through discipline in small things, the greater tasks that once seemed difficult become easier. For example, it takes discipline to sit at my desk each day with my water and a sanguine and ebullient attitude to write this book. As the days go by, however, the writing becomes more enjoyable, and I see my vision of a book come to fruition.

We can't address the topic of discipline without also bringing in the power of conditioning. The way we have been conditioned to behave affects all areas of our lives. For example, choosing foods that support well-being requires repeated reinforcement of such choices. When you continually repeat a negative or unhealthy habit (such as eating ice cream each night for dessert), it develops into a bad habit. *To eradicate your negative conditions, to break bad habits and to strengthen your self-discipline, make a twenty-one-day agreement with yourself.* Let's say that at mealtime you want to stop eating before you feel stuffed (overeating stresses every organ and cell in the body). Resolve to stick with your agreement every day for twenty-one days. If you skip a day, you must begin the twenty-one-day cycle again. Behavioral scientists say it takes twenty-one days to form a new habit or break an old one. After twenty-one days, your mind and body stop resisting the change you're trying to make. Twenty-one days isn't a very long time. If you find your mind coming up with excuses, as it will, you can maintain discipline by reminding yourself that you have to continue for only twenty-one days.

I have been punctilious about incorporating this twenty-one-day program into my life for 30 years. On the first day of each month, I make an agreement with myself to give up some unhealthful habit or to cultivate a new or upgraded positive pattern. In this way, I make 12 beneficial changes in my life each year.

Keeping your agreements with yourself boosts your self-esteem. I know how I feel when I say I'm going to do something and I don't follow through on it. I feel lousy. When I stay disciplined and do what I say I'm going to do, I feel empowered. I have great respect for people who keep their word. I lose respect for those who don't. I have a few friends who make a habit of saying they are going to do something, like start exercising regularly or eating more fresh fruits and vegetables. But when I check with them to see how they're progressing, I hear a litany of excuses.

One thing that can undermine your ability to stay focused, disciplined, and positive is not getting enough sleep, which leads to the next surefire choice.

3. SLEEP YOUR WAY TO YOUTHFUL VITALITY

There is nothing more restorative for your body than a good night's sleep, night after night after night. Consistent lack of sleep can lead to a variety of health problems, including toxic buildup, weight gain and accelerated aging, depression, irritability and impatience, low sex drive, memory loss, lethargy, relationship problems, accidents and at least 1,500 reported "drowsy driving" fatalities each year. Studies reveal that *driving on only 6 hours of sleep is like driving drunk*. Cars are so cozy and comfortable these days, and cruise control doesn't help. The instant you feel drowsy at the wheel of an automobile—when your eyelids get heavy—get off the road!

People are sleeping less now than they did a century ago, thanks to electric lighting and the shift to an urban, industrialized economy, not to mention late-night television. The result is a disruption of basic body metabolism. With workloads and daily stress increasing for many of us, sleep issues loom larger than ever. Let's take a brief look at sleep and how lack of it affects us as individuals and as a society.

At the University of Chicago, Karine Spiegel and colleagues asked research participants to stay in bed just four hours per night for six nights, then twelve hours per night for the next seven nights. When subjects were sleep deprived, their blood sugars, cortisol and sympathetic nervous system activity rose, and thyrotropin, which regulates thyroid function, fell. In other words, the results of this study show that chronic sleep deprivation forces the body into a fight-or-flight response, pushing blood sugars and other hormone-related functions out of kilter.

Higher cortisol levels, among other things, lead to memory loss, an increase in fat storage and a decrease in muscle—the perfect combination if you want to lower metabolism and gain weight easily. But if you want to increase muscle mass, which is necessary to create a fit, lean, healthy body, you need at least 7-8 hours of sound sleep nightly to encourage muscle maintenance and growth and the release of the human growth hormone, which helps keep you youthful and strong. Put another way, *sleeping more can make you slimmer.*

Sleep deprivation also may accelerate the aging process. In the same Spiegel study, participants who only slept 4 hours per night for one week metabolized glucose 40 percent more slowly than usual, which is similar to the rate seen in elderly people. Glucose metabolism quickly returned to normal after participants got a full night's sleep every night for a week.

So how do you know if you are sleep deprived? World renowned sleep expert Dr. William C. Dement, author of *The Promise of Sleep*, says that if you become sluggish, drowsy or fatigued, particularly after lunch or in the middle of the afternoon, you are sleep deprived. If you have difficulty getting up in the morning—one of my clients often sleeps through two alarms—you're sleep deprived.

Ninety-five percent of Americans suffer from a sleep disorder at some time in their lives, and 60 percent suffer from some persistent sleep disorder, according to Dement's research. When it comes to sleep, he says, *most people require a minimum of eight hours nightly.* Every hour you lose adds to your sleep indebtedness, and you cannot expect to catch up by sleeping late one day a week. The lost sleep accumulates progressively and contributes to long-term health problems. And this doesn't just pertain to adults. Children and teens actually need even more sleep than adults. Sleep loss affects how they learn, causes accidents, increases the likelihood of depression and can lead to violent or aggressive behavior.

Recognizing that many of us simply can't get to bed any earlier or get up any later, I recommend napping. A few enlightened businesses are adopting the pioneering view that napping actually can promote productivity. Some companies even provide special nap rooms for employees. Naps should be recognized as a powerful tool in battling fatigue. However, if you have insomnia, naps can actually aggravate your night's sleep. By taking the edge off your sleepiness, an afternoon nap may make it even harder for you to sleep at night. In other words, if you are sleepy because of insomnia, napping should be *avoided*.

Naps are also *not* recommended after meals. It's natural to want to nap after eating because distension of the stomach from the meal increases the deep-sleep drive. The problem is that if you overeat, the digestive process may interfere with the *quality* of your sleep, and conversely, sleep may interfere with the digestive process. You are better off to allow digestion to occur *before* sleeping, since both digestion and sleep tend to work better when performed separately.

Here are five tips for better sleep.

1. Morning exercise helps you sleep at night. If you're not a morning person, exercise at least 4 hours before bedtime—any closer and you'll be too revved up.

2. Increase evening body heat for deeper sleep. A hot bath, sauna, or Jacuzzi two hours before bedtime increases melatonin as the body temperature drops. This overall increased body temperature, with its accompanying big drop back to normal, helps promote sound, deep sleep. (See page 81 on Infrared Saunas.)

3. Make sure the bed is for sleep and sex only. Avoid working, eating or watching TV in bed. Reading until you fall asleep is okay, but try to read inspirational, uplifting or calming books.

4. Create a conducive environment. Sleep in natural fiber pajamas in a dark and quiet room, with fresh air and green plants. A cool room and cool pillow are also helpful. Two or three drops of pure essential lavender oil on your pillow promotes relaxation and calm. And, of course, a good mattress and a few pillows are essential.

5. Don't eat or drink liquids too close to bedtime. Choose your evening meals wisely. Large, spicy meals within 2–3 hours of bedtime undermine deep sleep. Alcohol is a stimulant and blocks the restful sleep experienced during the REM (rapid eye movement) cycle. While I advocate drinking several glasses of purified, alkaline water throughout the day, cut off your water intake within two hours of bedtime to cut down on nighttime bathroom visits and to take extra stress off your kidneys. Sweet dreams!

4. HYDRATE YOUR BODY WITH PURIFIED, ALKALINE WATER

Without water, life does not exist. Before scientists look for any form of life on other planets, they first look for any sign of water. Over 70 percent of our body weight is water; that's about 10 gallons of water for a 120-pound person. We're bundles of water wrapped in skin standing on two feet.

Water is a strong solvent that carries many invisible ingredients: minerals, oxygen, nutrients, waste products, pollutants, etc. Inside the human body, blood (90 percent of which is water) circulates throughout the body distributing nutrients and oxygen, and collecting wastes and carbon dioxide. Every substance deep in our body was brought there by blood ("the river of life") and can be carried out by blood. When a person loses 20 pounds of weight through a diet program, that 20 pounds of substance comes out of the body through urine, which is why any diet program requires drinking a lot of water.

Water is very important in helping to maintain a healthy metabolic rate. At least 2 quarts a day, between meals, is essential—more if you're physically very active. That's at least 8 glasses of water daily. Freshly-squeezed fruit or vegetable juices and natural teas without caffeine can count towards your water tally. But not all liquid is alike. Some are wet but are actually *anti*water. Alcohol, sodas, coffee and other caffeinated beverages act as diuretics, thus increasing your need for more water during the day.

We often turn to food when we're really just thirsty. Water makes you feel fuller and suppresses your appetite naturally. Have a large glass of water about 15 to 20 minutes before each meal or snack. If you are interested in losing some body fat, listen up. Simply drinking purified, alkaline water—between 8 and 12 glasses of water a day, and not changing anything else—not food or exercise—helps with fat loss and reshaping the body.

The liver's main functions are detoxification and regulation of metabolism. The kidneys can get rid of toxins and spare the liver if they have sufficient water. This allows the liver to metabolize more fat. Adequate water also will decrease bloating and edema caused by fluid accumulation by flushing out sodium, acidic wastes and other toxins. A high water intake also helps relieve constipation by keeping your stools soft. Your urine should be clear, light-colored and plentiful. Drink even more in hot weather, low humidity (such as desert environments or air traveling), high altitude, when you're ill or stressed, when you want to accelerate fat loss or when you're pregnant.

The best water to drink, in my estimation, is purified water. A few drops of fresh lemon juice in water is my favorite way to drink it. It adds to the taste, increases the nutritional value and assists in healing and detoxification. Lemon in hot water first thing in the morning is an excellent laxative. Make a habit of drinking water. According to a recent survey, the reason most people don't drink as much as they know they ought to, is lack of time or being too busy. Decide to

drink water before every meal. Set objectives for yourself such as drinking before you leave the house, and first thing upon your return or before you start work. Take water breaks instead of coffee breaks. Strive to drink one-half ounce daily for every pound you weigh. Thus, a 150-pound person drinks 75 ounces, or approximately 2.5 quarts. Here's my general rule of thumb: Drink one glass every hour so that your urine comes out clear, not dark yellow.

5. ALKALIZE & ENERGIZE

In his popular book, *Alkalize or Die*, author and friend Dr. Theodore A. Baroody writes about the importance of living a lifestyle that supports alkalinity. When foods are eaten, they are broken down into small nutrients and delivered to each and every cell in the body. These nutrients are burned with oxygen in a slow, controlled manner to supply the necessary energy for us to function. After oxidation, these nutrients become waste products. Gourmet or junk food, *all* foods make waste products. The difference between healthful food and unhealthful food is the amount and kind of wastes produced: acid or alkaline. Human cells die in about four weeks: some regenerate and some are destroyed. Dead cells are waste products. All waste products need to be discarded from the body, mostly through urine and perspiration. Most of these wastes are acidic; therefore, when we excrete them, our urine is acidic and our skin is acidic.

Most of us overwork, stay up late, get up early and stress ourselves to the limit without giving ourselves time to rest. Most people like to eat meat and refined grains and enjoy colas and other soft drinks, which are all highly acidic foods and drinks. Furthermore, the polluted environment kills our healthy cells, thus producing more acidic wastes. This means that we cannot get rid of 100 percent of the acidic wastes that we make daily, and these leftover wastes are stored somewhere within our bodies.

Since our blood and cellular fluids must be slightly alkaline to sustain life, the body converts liquid acidic wastes into solid wastes. Solidification of liquid acid wastes is the body's defense mechanism to survive. Some of these acid wastes include cholesterol, fatty acid, uric acid, kidney stones, phosphates, sulfates, urates and gallstones, and they accumulate in many places throughout our body.

One of the biggest problems caused by the buildup of acidic wastes is the fact that *acid coagulates blood*. When blood becomes thicker, it clogs up the capillaries, which is why so many adult diseases require blood thinners as part of their treatment. It is commonly known that degenerative diseases are caused by poor blood circulation. Where there is an accumulation of acidic wastes, and the local capillaries are clogged, any organ(s) in that area will not be getting an adequate blood supply, eventually leading to dysfunction of that organ(s).

Doctors have found that more than 150 degenerative diseases are associated with acidity, including cancer, diabetes, arthritis, heart disease, and gall and kidney stones. All diseases thrive in an acidic, oxygen-poor environment.

The symbol "pH" (power of hydrogen) is a measurement of how acidic or alkaline a substance is. The pH scale goes from 1–14. For example, a reading of 1 pH would be acidic, a reading of 7 pH would be neutral and a reading of 14 pH would be alkaline.

Keep in mind that a drop in every point on the pH scale is 10 times more acid (i.e., from 7 to 6 is 10 times, from 7 to 5 is 100 times, etc.). From 7 to 2 is 100,000 times more acidic! And sodas are in the acidic range of 2 pH. Over the long term, the effects of sodas are devastating to the body. Acidity, sugars and artificial sweeteners can shorten your life. In fact, *it takes 32 glasses of alkaline water at a pH of 9 to neutralize the acid from one 12 ounce cola or soda.* When you drink sodas, the body uses up reserves of its own stored alkaline buffers—mainly calcium from the bones and DNA—to raise the body's alkalinity levels, especially to maintain proper blood alkaline pH levels. Acidic blood levels can cause death!

The **Ionizer Plus** is my #1 health secret to staying hydrated and vibrantly healthy, along with my Infrared Sauna—also from High Tech Health. For more information, or to purchase a top-quality **Ionizer Plus** or **Infrared Sauna,** visit: **HighTech Health.com** or call: **800-794-5355 MT**. Mention my name to get a $300 discount on your purchase of the **Ionizer Plus** (and $500 off the purchase of an **Infrared Sauna**).

If you want to know your current acid-alkaline balance, you can check your pH with a simple saliva test by using litmus paper that comes with a color chart. To properly check your saliva pH, bring up your saliva twice and spit it out. Bring it up a third time, but don't spit it out. Put the litmus strip under your tongue and wet it with your saliva. To find your pH level, match the color of the litmus strip to the corresponding color on the chart. Your goal is to have an alkaline (7.1–7.5) pH level. Note that it is natural for you to be more alkaline in the morning and more acidic at night.

Most of the degenerative diseases we call "old-age diseases," like memory loss, osteoporosis, arthritis, diabetes and hypertension, are actually lifestyle diseases caused by acidosis, an overall poor diet (especially a lack of leafy green vegetables), improper digestion and too much stress.

So how can you alkalize your body? Baroody suggests following an 80 percent/20 percent dietary rule. Choose 80 percent alkaline-forming foods and drinks and 20 percent acid-forming foods and drinks for vibrant health. His best-selling book, *Alkalize or Die*, breaks down all the foods in categories of acid, alkaline or neutral. In a nutshell, most fruits and vegetables are alkaline and most other foods, including meat, dairy, fish, fowl, grains, seeds and nuts are acid-forming, with a few exceptions. He recommends as an optimum diet building up to eating 75 percent fresh and raw plant-based foods and 25 percent cooked foods. He encourages the daily practice of meditation, deep breathing, exercise, deep sleep and positive thinking—all of which increase alkalinity.

One of the quickest and best ways to improve health and increase alkalinity is to make fresh vegetable juice every day. Chlorophyll, which gives green vegetables their color, builds the blood and powerfully alkalizes the system. I cover the importance of juicing on my website and in my books *Living on the Lighter Side, Body Temple Vitality* and *The Curative Kitchen & Lifestyle*.

As well, visit my website, **SusanSmithJones.com**, to learn more about the healing power of alkaline water (I have several articles on the site) and the *Ionizer Plus Electrolyzer Water System* by High Tech Health in Boulder, CO. This purifying and alkalizing water device (I've had the same one in my kitchen for over 20 years) will make a positive difference in your body by increasing your alkalinity, immunity and energy, and helping to rejuvenate your body and look younger.

6. HEAL WITH HEAT THERAPY & AN INFRARED SAUNA

Researchers from Saxion University of Applied Science in the Netherlands found that infrared sauna treatments can help reverse chronic pain with little to no side effects. They studied the effects of infrared saunas in patients with rheumatoid arthritis and ankylosing spondylitis over a four-week period, with a series of eight treatments using infrared saunas. Sauna therapy was well-tolerated with no adverse effects, and they found that a significant percentage of patients experienced decreased symptoms of pain and stiffness.

Fatigue also decreased in both groups of patients compared to before beginning treatment, leading the researchers to conclude that infrared treatment has statistically significant short-term beneficial effects in patients experiencing pain without causing any worsening disease symptoms or unwanted side effects.

Who can benefit from Infrared Saunas?

Researchers have been studying the effects of saunas for decades when it comes to pain management and relaxation. Infrared saunas are relatively new compared to conventional saunas but have picked up attention recently for helping naturally treat multiple health problems with little to no side effects. Some studies have shown benefits of infrared sauna therapy for people with:

✓ Cardiovascular disease

✓ Rheumatoid arthritis

✓ Diabetes

✓ Chronic fatigue

✓ Obesity

✓ Poor digestion

✓ High blood pressure

✓ Depression and anger

✓ Congestive heart failure

✓ Chronic muscle and joint pains

One of the biggest benefits of infrared saunas is that they're comfortable and simple to use, even for people who struggle with pain or who have sensitive skin and stomachs when it comes to heat, all with no need for medications or doctor visits.

Why infrared? Because its radiant heat is known to penetrate the skin more deeply than traditional saunas, better aiding in a number of restorative body processes. Here are just a few ways infrared saunas can benefit your body—and why I encourage my clients, family and friends to make them part of their health-supporting routines.

You'll flush out toxins

Saunas, infrared or otherwise, make you sweat. Sweating helps flush out toxins from the body and in so doing reduces its toxic load. With infrared saunas, the sweating is deeper and more profuse, enabling your body to excrete a higher percentage of toxins than with a conventional sauna. Infrared saunas are also a great alternative for those who don't like high temperatures or need to avoid them for medical reasons. The gentler heat of infrared saunas runs roughly 20–60 degrees lower, making them easier to tolerate. But no matter which type you choose, remember to get the OK from your doctor first before diving into a regular sauna routine.

Blood pressure will lower and muscles will unwind, without a pharmaceutical assist

You don't have to sit in an infrared sauna for hours on end to reap the benefits. For most people, all that's needed is a few 15-20 minute sessions a week. During your sauna, as you sweat, you'll be stimulating better flood flow and circulation throughout your body. That increased circulation will help lower blood pressure, and make you feel good all over, relaxing tight muscles and easing minor aches and pains to boot. If you're troubled by muscle or joint pain, or more chronic conditions like arthritis, infrared heat from the sauna can provide drug-free pain relief, reducing stiffness and inflammation. In addition, it has also been shown to improve the functioning of the endothelial cells lining the arteries.

Cut a cold or flu off at the pass

Feeling like you're on the verge of getting sick? I recommend that you head to the nearest infrared sauna (preferably in your home) as early as possible. Why? Because the infrared's radiant heat will stimulate circulation, rev up the production of white blood cells and rally your immune system's response to invaders. All that action will make your body a much less hospitable environment for germs to grow—and a great place for them to die. Even if you're not on the verge of coming down with something, remember that infrared saunas, and the increased circulation that comes with regular use, are also great for speeding muscle recovery, too.

Look younger, no "beauty" creams required

Infrared saunas offer a wonderful bonus for the skin: they help improve skin tone and reduce signs of aging by stimulating better circulation, blood flow and increased collagen production—all of which improve the look of your skin. The increased circulation, elimination of toxins and flushing out of cellular debris enhance overall skin health, giving it a more radiant appearance, without a trip to your local beauty supply store.

Drop a little weight effortlessly

The plentiful sweating you'll do during a sauna session will register immediately on the scale as weight loss. However, most of the weight loss will be "water weight" which will return when you re-hydrate. However, there is evidence that infrared saunas, because of their ability to penetrate the skin more deeply, increase metabolic rate and can help the body burn off anywhere from 200—600 calories in a half hour session. Keep in mind though, while a regular infrared sauna routine won't melt off a spare tire, it can support a sensible diet and exercise plan by giving your metabolism a little extra boost while you literally sit and relax. And remember, hydration is essential if you're using infrared (or conventional) saunas, so never skimp on liquids just for the sake of seeing lower numbers on the scale. Drink up before, during and after—no exceptions! When I use my *Transcend* or *Thermal Life Infrared Saunas* by High Tech Health, I always bring in with me a quart of fresh alkaline water with lemon slices in it.

Please refer to my website, **SusanSmithJones.com** for detailed information on Infrared Saunas and how this heat therapy heals the body from head to toe. The company, High Tech Health in Boulder, CO, offers the best Infrared Saunas in the industry. Their ***Thermal Life Infrared Sauna*** is in my office and their ***Transcend Infrared Sauna*** is in my home. Both are the highest quality possible and have been front and center in my healthy living program for 20 years. They come in all different sizes.

Whether you put your personal sauna in your spare bedroom, on your backyard deck, in your garage, bathroom or basement, in the garden, or even in the corner of your bedroom, regular use will supercharge your healing, health and rejuvenation. It's my #1 health secret to never getting sick and always maintaining my youthful vitality, along with the alkaline water from my *Ionizer Plus* device—also from High Tech Health.

For more information, or to purchase a top-quality Infrared Sauna, visit: **HighTechHealth.com** or call: **800-794-5355 MT**. Mention my name to get a $500 discount on your purchase of a sauna (and $300 off the purchase of an *Ionizer Plus*).

7. PRACTICE THE ART OF RELAXATION & DEEP BREATHING

One of the world's leading experts on the brain is the former Harvard medical doctor, Herbert Benson, MD, author of *The Relaxation Response*. What Benson calls "the relaxation response" is the body's ability to enter into a state characterized by an overall reduction of the metabolic rate and a lowered heart rate. According to Benson, this state of relaxation also acts as a door to a renewed mind, a changed life and a feeling of awareness. He describes the physiological changes that occur when you are relaxed as a harmonizing or increased communication between the two sides of the brain, resulting in feelings often described as well-being, unboundedness, infinite connection and peak experience.

One way to cultivate calmness and peacefulness is to progressively relax your body, beginning with your toes and ending with your head. Breathe slowly and deeply, and totally relax each part of your body, saying to yourself as you go along, "My toes, feet, legs [and so on] are relaxed," until you have gone through your entire body. Then rest for a while in the quiet and silence. Listening to a relaxation or meditation tape also may be helpful. (You can find out more about my own relaxation audio programs by visiting the Store on my website.)

Here's another great tip you can easily do at work or at home to help relax your mind and body. Look at a picture of a beautiful landscape.

Yes, it's that simple! Two studies measured the effect of certain photographic images on emotional and physiological responses. The first study was designed to find ways of fighting the boredom and homesickness that astronauts experience during extended stays in space. Researchers projected a variety of slides on the walls of a room built to simulate a space station and recorded the subjects' responses to various scenes. The second study focused on hospital patients who were about to undergo surgery. In both groups, pictures of spacious views and glistening water lowered heart rates and produced feelings of calmness.

An easy and inexpensive way to look at a beautiful landscape is to get a poster. I have a Sierra Club poster in my prayer/meditation room that has a dazzling view of water, mountains and colorful wildflowers. Every time I look at it, I feel more relaxed. This is the perfect solution if you work in an office without windows. Larger posters of resplendent nature scenes can transform a room and provide you with a mini-fantasy vacation whenever you need it.

I also highly recommend getting one of those "sound soothers" that offer a variety of nature sounds, everything from gentle rain, to ocean waves, and a flowing brook, to a waterfall, an aviary and wind chimes. I use mine daily. In fact, on my website, I have a page that offers all of these nature sounds and more that you can enjoy any time you wish by clicking the button.

Deep Breathing

Can you breathe your way to vibrant health? In most cases, I think you can. How often do you pause to consider the intricacies of breathing? Breathing is perhaps the only physiological process that can be either voluntary or involuntary. One can breathe, making their breath do whatever they wish, or one can ignore it, and after a while the body simply begins to breathe on its own. Breathing becomes reflexive. The body can't operate without breathing, so if conscious control of the breath is abandoned, then some unconscious part of the mind begins functioning, picks it up and starts breathing for us. Something is triggered in the lower part of the brain. But in this case, breathing falls back under the control of primitive parts of the brain, the unconscious realms of the mind, where emotions, thoughts and feelings (of which we may have little or no awareness) become involved. These wreak havoc with breath rhythms. In other words, the breath becomes haphazard and often irregular if we lose conscious control of it. It's important to bring breath back into your awareness so it's re-integrated into your consciousness.

Are your breaths rapid and shallow? Take a minute now to check and see how many breaths per minute you take (count both the inhalation and exhalation as one breath). If it is between 16-20, then you are most likely a thoracic breather. This means that your breaths are not getting to the lower part of your lungs but remain fairly high in the chest. Thoracic breathing is the least efficient and most common type.

Diaphragmatic or deep abdominal breathing, on the other hand, promotes a more relaxed state. Take a long, slow, deep breath right now. Visualize the air filling the lower part of the lungs. Since gravity pulls more blood into that area, the most efficient passage of oxygen into the blood occurs there, slowing the breath as the body gets more oxygen. It's important to note how closely tied are respiration and the heart. As the breath slows (to 6–8 breaths per minute) and deepens, the heart's job is made considerably easier. There is evidence to suggest that diaphragmatic breathing is beneficial because it increases the suction pressure created in the thoracic cavity and improves the venous return of blood, thereby reducing the load on the heart and enhancing circulatory function. Also, diaphragmatic breathing has the added bonus of relaxing the muscles of the ribs, chest and stomach.

Diaphragmatic breathing is really quite simple. It's the habit of doing it that must be consciously cultivated before it can become automatic. A simple practice to achieve this is to lie down on your back on your bed or a mat or rug, with one palm placed on the center of the chest and the other on the lower edge of the rib cage where the abdomen begins. As you inhale, the lower edge of the rib cage should expand and the abdomen should rise; as you exhale, the opposite should occur; there should be relatively little movement of the upper chest. By practicing diaphragmatic breathing, you will find in time that this exercise is becoming habitual and automatic.

So choose to cultivate the habit of deep breathing. In order to make deep breathing automatic in my life, I tried this experiment several years ago. I set my watch to beep every hour (except when I was sleeping, of course) and I took one to three minutes to do some deep breathing. As the days and weeks went on, I noticed that when the hourly beep came around, I was already practicing deep breathing; it was increasingly becoming a habit and a conscious choice. Now, most of the time, diaphragmatic breathing is my natural way to breathe.

Simply put: Developing harmonious and rhythmic breathing along with diaphragmatic breathing will have health benefits and can improve your quality of life. I have always found that when I'm relaxed, calm and balanced and have been breathing deeply on a regular basis, it's easier to live in the moment and laugh at myself and all the incongruities of daily life.

8. BE IN THE PRECIOUS PRESENT & LAUGH OFTEN

Living *in* the moment is different from living *for* the moment. Young children seem to be masters of getting totally involved in and focused on whatever they are doing right now. Granted, their attention span is not long, but they are able to focus on whatever is taking place in their lives at the moment. When they eat, they just eat; when they play, they just play; when they talk, they just talk. They throw themselves wholeheartedly into their activities.

Have you ever noticed that young children are willing to try anything at a moment's notice? Even though they might have experienced that same thing before, they will express wide-eyed excitement and wonderment. Children don't use a yardstick to measure activities or compare the present with the past. They know they've played the game

before, or had someone read the same story just last night, yet the game or the story is still as fresh and as wonderful as it was the first time.

Think about your attitude when doing the dishes, vacuuming or watering the plants. You probably find these activities boring. But a child can't wait to participate, and acts as though it's just about the most exciting thing he or she has ever done. What a wonderful quality that is! To be excited about life—about every part of life as though it's always fresh and new. Actually, it is. It's only old thoughts and distorted attitudes that get in the way of celebrating each moment.

One way to be mindful of the present moment is to focus on your breathing, as elucidated above. "Conscious breathing, which is a powerful meditation in its own right," writes Eckhart Tolle in the sagacious book, *The Power of Now,* "will gradually put you in touch with the body. Follow the breath with your attention as it moves in and out of your body. Breathe into the body, and feel your abdomen expanding and contracting slightly with each inhalation and exhalation. If you find it easy to visualize, close your eyes and see yourself surrounded by light or immersed in a luminous substance—a sea of consciousness. Then breathe in that light." I do this exercise a few times each week to help me remember to be in the present moment. I visualize myself surrounded by God's light and love.

This precious present moment is the only moment we'll ever have. It's our moment of power and all there is in life. In this moment, problems do not exist. It is here we find our joy and balance and are able to embrace our true selves. It is here we discover that we are already complete and perfect. If we are able to be fully present and take each step in the "Now," we will be opening ourselves to the transforming experience of the power of the present. "When your attention is in the present moment, you enjoy life more intensely because you are fully alive," writes Don Miguel Ruiz in another one of my favorite books, *The Four Agreements*. I like that a lot. You enjoy life more intensely because you are fully alive! How alive and present are you to the Now in your life?

Have you ever driven to work or run errands and not remembered how you got there? Check in with yourself every hour or so. Are you slouching? How's your attitude? What are you thinking? Is your breathing shallow? Don't wait until your shoulders are up around your ears before you try to relax. Learn to be mindful about how you're feeling and what's happening around you. I usually describe mindfulness as developing the mind's capacity to attain a balanced, awake understanding of what's happening, knowing how you feel about it, and choosing your wisest response. In my estimation, your wisest response—no matter what's going on in your life at the moment—is to embrace a cheerful attitude.

Along with my faith in God, meditation/prayer time, being in nature and living in the present moment, laughter is another one of my favorite ways to mollify stress.

It is okay to laugh, even when times are tough. Toxic worry almost always entails a loss of perspective; a sense of humor almost always restores it. I love the delightful *Ellen Degeneres Show*. I find Ellen's sense of humor and attitude about life inspiring and uplifting, and I always feel better after watching it. Also, think of the late president Ronald Reagan; he was popular and beloved partly because of his innate kindness with others, his fetching sense of humor and his propensity to see the glass as half full—to focus on the positive and a hopeful future. Making people laugh and being sanguine and optimistic are endearing and disarming qualities.

It was Norman Cousins, a noted journalist and author who, during a life-threatening illness, was able to achieve two hours of pain-free living for every ten minutes he devoted to laughter. In his renowned book, *Anatomy of an Illness*, he told about how he watched old comedies by the Marx Brothers and the Three Stooges and *Candid Camera* by the hour. He learned that laughter—hearty belly laughter—produced certain chemicals in the brain that benefit body, mind and emotions.

You've probably already noticed or read my *Humor Time* sections found between the different parts of this book. According to researchers, laughter releases endorphins into the body that act as natural stress beaters. Laughter also aids most—and probably all—major systems of the body. A good laugh gives the heart muscles a good workout, improves circulation, fills the lungs with oxygen-rich air, clears the respiratory passages, stimulates alertness hormones that stimulate various tissues and alters the brain by diminishing tension in the central nervous system. It also helps relieve pain and counteracts fear, anger, and depression—all of which are linked to physical illness and stress.

Recently, the results of a scientific study on the power of laughter were trumpeted on all the major television news stations. The study results disclosed that *one minute of laughter boosts the immune system for 24 hours! And one minute of anger suppresses immunity for 6 hours!* The elixir of life—and the best way to soften your heart and diminish the wrinkles around your soul (and on your face!)—is hearty laughter. Laughter is a sterling stress buster and loving gift we can give ourselves and others in our lives. Laughter is calorie- and pain-free and costs nothing; the dividends are priceless.

Another superlative way to relieve pain and depression, improve circulation, reduce stress and help balance your body and life is through a positive attitude.

9. CULTIVATE AN ATTITUDE OF GRATITUDE

Choose to be positive and grateful every day. The link between mind and body has been contemplated since the time of Plato, but it's only recently that research has been done on the neurophysiology of the brain. *Every* thought transmits instructions to the body through some 70 trillion nerve cells, so when you think a negative thought, your immune system is immediately compromised. By the same token, when you think positive thoughts, your immune system is enhanced and your whole body benefits. Furthermore, an anxious or fearful mind instructs the body to be likewise—tense and nervous. A calm mind creates a calm body.

Keep your thoughts imbued with your highest vision of how you'd like to live and what you want to experience in life. In other words, visualize your goals and dreams. Dream big! Regardless of circumstances, always be persistent and keep the faith because *you can create your heart's desires.* You are full of infinite possibilities; whatever you can imagine, you can accomplish. It was Paramahansa Yogananda who wrote "You can accomplish anything if you do not accept limitations . . . whatever you make up your mind to do, you can do." Similarly, in his books *Jonathan Livingston Seagull* and *Illusions,* author Richard Bach writes that you are never given a wish without also being given

the ability to make it come true. And it was the mythologist Joseph Campbell who offered the following exquisite advice: *Follow your bliss.* When I pay attention to and honor the stirrings of my heart and soul, I look and feel younger. We age quickly when we live with regret instead of cultivating our highest visions and dreams.

So choose your thoughts wisely. A new report from the *Mayo Proceedings* suggests that individuals who profess pessimistic explanations for life events have poorer physical health and a higher mortality rate compared with either optimists or "middle-of-the-road" types, regardless of age or sex. In fact, every 10-point increase in the study's pessimism scores was associated with a 19 percent increase in the risk of death. Conversely, participants whose test scores indicated optimism had a survival rate significantly better than expected. The reason for this may be that pessimists may be more "passive" or have a "darker" outlook on life than other personality types, leaving them more prone to bad life events—such as illness, injury and depression. The researchers concluded that pessimism itself is a "risk factor" for early death, and should be viewed in the same way as other risk factors, such as obesity, high blood pressure or high cholesterol level.

When you find one thing, however small, to be thankful for and you hold that feeling for as little as *15 seconds*, research reveals that many subtle and beneficial physiologic changes take place in your body, including the following four:

1. Stress hormone levels of cortisol and norepinephrine decrease, creating a cascade of beneficial metabolic changes such as an enhanced immune system;

2. Coronary arteries relax, thus increasing the blood supply to your heart;

3. Heart rhythm becomes more harmonious, which positively affects your mood and all other bodily organs;

4. Breathing becomes deeper, thus increasing the oxygen level of your tissues.

If all of this happens when you focus for just 15 seconds on something that brings you pleasure, joy or a feeling of gratitude, imagine what would happen to your health if you were able to cultivate grateful thoughts and feelings regularly, at least once per hour throughout each day of the year. The health benefits of gratitude (which is really the same thing as love) are an amazing example of how connected the bridge between the mind, body and emotions really is and how simple it is to put this connection to work in your own life. But, as you well know, simple isn't necessarily easy. Like everything important in life, you must make a conscious choice and take action.

Gratitude (and appreciation) is a magnetic force that draws more good to each one of us. It's a dynamic spiritual energy that allows you to exert a powerful influence on your body, life and world. Most importantly, it's a stellar stress-buster. What you think about consistently, you bring about in your life. Another way of saying this is... *Where your focus goes, energy flows.* Keep a gratitude journal and each day write down at least three things for which you are grateful. Focusing on the positive things, even during the most difficult times, is the perfect remedy to reduce and alleviate stress. And if you don't feel positive and grateful, "fake it until you make it," as the saying goes. In other words, "acting as if" will help you through many challenging times and carry you on to better times. It was Shakespeare who championed this sage advice in his immortal words in *Hamlet:* "Assume a virtue, if you have it not."

> Always remember that a bad attitude can literally block love, blessing and destiny from finding you. Don't be the reason you don't succeed. Keep your attitude at a high altitude.

One of the countless things I'm grateful for in my life is my friendships with others. I treasure the feeling of being surrounded by tenderhearted people.

10. HONOR FRIENDSHIPS & BE TENDERHEARTED

I highly value and feel a great sense of gratitude for the love and support I receive from my friends, and for the opportunity to care deeply for others. The way to have a friend is to be one. Friends help sustain us when we're down, comfort us when we're sad and offer counsel when we're confused. Friends are truly the best kind of wealth we can have—a wealth not calculated in numbers, but in the priceless value of love and kindness. Show comity, love and appreciation for your friends. Never take your friends for granted. Friendship is as sacred a commitment as any: our friends are sent by God, so that we can help them and they can help us.

Often in today's society we are tempted to put our selfish interests first, before loyalty or integrity or commitment to higher values. Since what emanates from us will come back to us at some point, this is ultimately not a winning attitude. True friendship can be one of the rewards. The love shared between two people is the most precious gift we have. I appreciate this thought by T.S. Eliot who wrote: "What do we live for, if not to make life easier for one another." Jesus taught his followers to love one another. David Craddock, who wrote this book's Foreword, reminds me from time to time that… "God comes to you in the guise of a true and noble friend to serve, inspire and guide you." That's what my friendships do for me. They also teach me the importance of being kind and gentle with others. Gentleness and kindness usually ride tandem.

According to Webster's latest edition, gentle means kindly, mild, amiable, not violent or severe. It means compassionate, considerate, tolerant, calm, mild-tempered, courteous and peaceful. But I think that the best synonym for gentle is tenderhearted. I really like that word. And I love being around people who are tenderhearted.

To be treated with tenderheartedness, we must first offer that quality to other people. Respond to others exactly as you would want to be treated. No one likes to be rushed or belittled, ignored or unappreciated. Everyone likes kindness, patience and respect. Ephesians 4:32 advises, "Be kind to one another, tenderhearted, forgiving one another..." As my mom always taught me, simple and mellifluous words like "please" and "thank you" are always welcome and much needed in our stress-filled lives.

In the heart-warming Steven Spielberg movie I watched recently, *The Terminal,* the character Viktor Navorski—beautifully portrayed by Tom Hanks—is a shining example of a tenderhearted person, someone you'd love to count as one of your friends.

Reaching out with a kind act or word of praise or appreciation can be so simple. Yet sometimes we assume that others "have it together," and do not need our kindness. Wouldn't it be better to move beyond our assumptions and to offer the kind of thoughtfulness we would appreciate receiving—a compliment, a smile, a hug, a pat on the shoulder, a note of thanks or just a question that shows concern? If your kind gesture goes unnoticed or is refused, it doesn't matter, because in giving to another, you give to yourself. You'll feel better. Gandhi said that the pure loving kindness of one gentle soul can nullify the hatred of millions. Because we live in such a turbulent world, it's more important than ever for all of us to live more tenderheartedly. It will bring more joy and balance to our planet.

Another wonderful way to bring more joy and balance to your life and the world is through the companionship of animal friends, such as dogs, cats, horses, birds, rabbits and fish. Studies show that people who live with pets are healthier than those who don't. Pet owners have lower cholesterol and triglyceride levels, and are less likely to suffer from nervousness, insomnia, stomachaches, headaches and other minor health problems. *New* pet owners, especially dog owners, experience an increase in psychological well-being, self-esteem and calmness. Consider opening your home to more animal friends.

11. MEDITATE & LIVE WITH QUIET REVERENCE & EQUANIMITY

Ralph Waldo Emerson knew the key to living with serenity and calmness. Meditation. It's a simple process of turning within and connecting with God—our inherent, ever-present source of love, peace, joy and inner guidance. Emerson offers us this sapient thought. "What lies behind us and what lies before us are small matters compared to what lies within us."

Take time each day to pray, meditate, talk to God and simply spend a few minutes in silence. Studies have found lower rates of depression and stress among those who believe in God. If you are not religious, meditate. Prayer and meditation help us keep things in perspective, keep our minds calm and our lives balanced. From Joshua 1:8 we read... *This book of the law shall not depart from your mouth, but you shall meditate on it day and night, so that you may be careful to do according to all that is written in it; for then you will make your way prosperous, and then you will have success.*

Practicing regular meditation is one of the best ways to bring stress hormone levels back to normal quickly, especially after an adrenaline-producing, cortisol-raising experience. I know of no more

effective way to bring about relaxation than through meditation—turning inward in silence and reconnecting with the peace and calmness that's always within you. Featured in a *Time* magazine cover story (August 4, 2003, *The Science of Meditation*), "meditation" is being embraced around the world because of its numerous physiological, mental, emotional and spiritual benefits.

When you think of meditation, you may envision crossed legs and chants of "ommmm," but meditation can be anything that helps you focus your attention and increase your awareness of your body and the silence within you. Personally, I meditate on the word of God, a passage in the Bible. Numerous scientific studies on meditation have shown it to cause a generalized reduction in many physiological and biochemical stress indicators, including decreases in heart rate, respiration rate, stress hormones and pulse rate, and increases in oxygen consumption and slow alpha waves (a brain wave associated with relaxation). It is now being used successfully by people suffering from chronic pain and chronic conditions such as cancer and heart disease, as well as stress-related disorders, including abdominal pain, chronic digestive disorders and ulcers.

For 35 years, I have been a disciplined meditator, and I teach workshops on the topic worldwide and work individually with individuals and families on simple ways to incorporate meditation into their lifestyle. For those of you who would like comprehensive information on meditation, its salutary benefits, and how to use it to reduce stress and achieve your goals, please refer to my audiobooks, *Choose to Live Peacefully* and *Wired to Meditate,* and my audio programs, *Celebrate Life!* and *Everyday Health—Pure & Simple,* all available from my website: **SusanSmithJones.com**.

Nurture this inner peacefulness by bookending your day with quiet meditation for at least 10-15 minutes first thing in the morning and again before you go to sleep at night. This quietude will remind you that you can make the choice every day to live in the world, but not be caught up in the frenzy of it. If we have peace within ourselves, we don't have to make an effort to spread it; we radiate it to whomever comes into our presence. Choose to make peace your "default" position in life.

Part of the meditation process is focused deep breathing. In fact, conscious breath—inhaling and exhaling slowly and deeply—is itself a form of meditation, as mentioned earlier. In addition to practicing deep breathing while meditating, take mini-breathing breaks throughout your day. While you're breathing, be sure to focus on your breath or a relaxing, peaceful and joyful thought, and not on anything that might be stressful.

Another aspect of meditation and living a balanced, healthy and joyful life is carving out moments of silence for yourself (as you do with meditation), even if it's only for a few minutes a day. Noise seems to part of our everyday lives—from the alarm clock in the morning and the traffic outside to the never-ending sounds of voices, radio and television, computers and gardening equipment. Our bodies and minds appear to acclimate to these outside intrusions. Or do they?

The Committee on Environmental Quality of the Federal Council for Science and Technology found that "growing numbers of researchers fear the dangerous and hazardous effects of intense noise on human health are seriously underestimated." The late Vice President Nelson Rockefeller, when writing about the environmental crisis of our time, noted that when people are fully aware of the damage noise can inflict on man, "Peace and quiet will surely rank along with clean skies and pure waters as top priorities for our generation."

More recent studies, highlighted in the informative book *Save Your Hearing Now*, by Michael D. Swidman, MD, FACS and Marie Moneysmith (what a great name!), suggest that we pay the price for adapting to noise—higher blood pressure, heart rate and adrenaline secretion, heightened aggression, impaired resistance to disease and a sense of helplessness. Studies indicate that when we can control noise, its effects are much less damaging.

I haven't been able to find any studies on the effects of quiet in repairing the stress of noise, but I know intuitively that most of us love quiet and need it desperately. We are so used to noise in our lives that silence can sometimes feel awkward and unsettling. On vacation, for instance, when quiet prevails, we may have trouble sleeping. But choosing times of silence can enrich the quality of our lives tremendously. If you find yourself overworked, stressed-out, irritated, tense or out of balance, rather than heading for a coffee or snack break, maybe all you need is a silence break.

Everyone at some time has experienced the feeling of being overwhelmed by life. Everyone, too, has felt the need to escape, to find a quiet, secluded place to experience the peace of Spirit, to be alone with quiet thoughts. Creating times of silence in your life takes commitment and discipline. Most of the time, *intervals of peaceful silence must be scheduled into your day's activities or you'll never have any.*

Maybe you can carve out times of silence while at home where you can be without radio, television, telephones or voices. If you live in a family, maybe the best quiet time for you is early in the morning before others arise. In that silence, you can become more aware, more sensitive to your surroundings and more in touch with the wholeness of life and your inherent inner guidance or intuition.

12. LISTEN TO YOUR INNER VOICE

Have you ever been thinking of someone you haven't heard from in a long time when suddenly that person called? Did you ever have the feeling that a friend was in trouble, and then contacted her and found out that she was, indeed? Or have you ever met someone and somehow knew that this person was going to be your spouse? Some call it a sixth sense, a hunch, a gut feeling, going on instinct or just knowing deep inside. Psychologists call it intuition—an obscure mental function that provides us with information so that we know without knowing how we know. I refer to it as God talking to us and giving us direction. It was Ralph Waldo Emerson who said: "Let us be silent that we may hear the whispers of God."

How tuned-in are you to this voice within? When you get a message, do you usually write it off as nothing? I have found from countless

experiences that as we pay attention to our intuition and act on what we hear or feel, we reduce stress and create more balance in our lives. The key here is not just getting the message, but listening to it and acting on it. According to Nancy Rosanoff, author of *Intuition Workout*, one study asked divorced couples when they first realized the relationship wasn't going to work out, and an astounding 80 percent replied, "before the wedding." Although something told them that the marriage was foolhardy, each couple stood together at the altar, either because they wished too strongly that their intuition was wrong, or they didn't identify the message as a kind of knowing they could trust.

So how can we develop the intuitive side of our being? The best way is just to sit still and listen. Turn within and pay attention. Too often we run away from ourselves, filling up our lives with constant, stress-filled activity. We don't take time to be still. Often creative geniuses report that their "real world" discoveries are nothing other than self-discoveries from a deep silence within. When someone asked William Blake where he got his ideas, he replied that he stuck his finger through the floor of heaven and pulled them down. Michelangelo spurned the congratulations that were proffered him after having turned a block of stone into a sculpture of a man by saying the man was in there all the time and just required a little help in getting out. Franz Kafka wrote: "There is no need to leave the house. Stay at your desk and listen. Don't even listen, just wait. Don't even wait, be perfectly still and alone. The world will unmask itself to you, it can't do otherwise. It will rise before you in raptures." There is a profound benefit to hitting the pause button on your life every so often to create mini-respites, enabling you to connect with your inner silence and power—the love and light of God within you.

Intuition can be nurtured in a variety of ways—through prayer, contemplation, walks in nature, time spent alone gazing out a window or thinking. The more you act on your intuitive hunches, the stronger and more readily available they become. As you become more sensitive to your oneness with Spirit, God and life, you will become more intuitive. Part of receiving those inner messages clearly comes when you learn to give up the analyzing, reasoning, doubting and limiting part of your mind. Practice makes perfect. And intuition is infallible when you anchor yourself in the consciousness of the Divine. In *The Tao of Pooh,* Benjamin Hoff shares: "The masters of life know the Way. They listen to the voice within them, the voice of wisdom and simplicity, the voice that reasons beyond cleverness and knows beyond knowledge. That voice is not just the power and property of a few, but has been given to everyone." And it was Helen Keller who gave us the following sagacious advice: "The most beautiful things in the world cannot be seen or even touched. They must be felt with the heart."

How can you simplify your life so that what's really important—what's really essential to live fully and celebrate life—can be uncovered and nurtured? This brings us to the last tip and choice for reducing stress and living a more balanced, joyful life.

13. SIMPLIFY YOUR PATH TO PEACE & LOVE

Simplify! What a wonderful word and a powerful process. The death of a dear friend recently made me sit down and think about life and about how I could choose to live more fully. The following words by Alfred D'Souze came to mind: "For a long time it had seemed to me that life was about to begin—real life. But there was always some obstacle in the way, something to be got through first, some unfinished business, time still to be served, a debt to be paid. Then life would begin. At last it dawned on me that these obstacles were my life."

This quote reminds me that sometimes our lives are so cluttered that it's difficult to see clearly. In the movie *Dances with Wolves,* I was deeply touched by the simplicity with which the Lakota Sioux people lived—able to gather all their belongings at a moment's notice and move on to another homeland. We are all trying to orchestrate the stresses, complexities and responsibilities of modern life. But much of the complexity we experience is, in fact, self-imposed. As we grow in self-awareness and live more internally, life gets simpler. Instead of getting our cues from the outside world, we listen for cues from our heart. Mahatma Gandhi encouraged each of us to: "Live simply, so that others may simply live." Jesus taught his followers not to be attached to material life, but instead to focus more on spiritual matters. He showed by example how to live a simple—but richly rewarding—life, unburdened by possessions.

Simplifying doesn't necessarily mean we have to restrict our activities, but it does mean uncluttering our lives so that we can put all our energy into activities we really care about. Activities, material things and relationships are all time and energy consumers. Maybe it's time to take inventory of your life and weed out the superfluous. Being simple with life—not naive, but clear—allows us to experience the present fully and deeply.

Plato wrote, "In order to seek one's own direction, one must simplify the mechanics of ordinary, everyday life." I like that. To begin uncluttering your life, start with your home. Weed out everything you don't need, want or use. Spend 15 minutes a day working on one area of your home, like a drawer or a closet. After your home is simplified, look at how you live, what you do and how you spend your time. For example, look at all the foods you eat in one meal. It's hard to appreciate any one of them fully when there are so many mixed together. Similarly, you could have a fantastic collection of art objects in your home worth millions of dollars, but if there are too many, it is difficult to appreciate each piece fully. By the same token, if you have too many obligations, details and responsibilities, life loses its luster. Follow the recommendation given by Henry David Thoreau in his classic book, *Walden,* "Our life is frittered away by detail.... Simplify, simplify."

Peace Pilgrim was another personification of simplicity. To the world, she may have seemed poor, walking penniless and wearing or carrying in her pockets her only material possessions. But she was indeed rich in blessings that no amount of money could buy—health, happiness and inner peace. Peace Pilgrim knew that material things come and go, that we can all survive quite comfortably with very little. The quality of our lives isn't created outside ourselves. It comes from a healthy self-image, inner joy and balance and our relationship with God. She wrote:

The simplified life is a sanctified life,
Much more calm, much less strife.
Oh, what wondrous truths are unveiled—
Projects succeed which had previously failed.
Oh, how beautiful life can be.
Beautiful simplicity.

In the book *Profound Healing,* author Cheryl Canfield related a story about simplicity that her friend Peace Pilgrim told her. The story was about a woman whose house burned down. She and her husband had been living in a big home where they had raised their family. After the fire, they moved into a house more suitable for just the two of them. Peace attempted to offer a word of sympathy, but the woman interrupted her and said, "Now I'll never have to clean out those closets, and I'll never have to clean out that attic." After telling this story, Peace wondered aloud if it wouldn't have been wiser to have simplified her home before the fire.

There was a time in my life when I found great pleasure in collecting material things. I would delight in buying lots of clothes, shoes, appliances, electronics, gadgets, books and cars until I got to the point where I was seeking fulfillment from what I collected rather than from God's light and love within me. In the pursuit of material possessions, I began to lose sight of the spiritual side of my nature through which all fulfillment, joy, peace and happiness come. I was looking outward to my collection of stuff for my value and worthiness as a human being rather than looking within.

Fortunately, I discovered that it's not what the world holds for you that's important, but what you bring to the world. When I realized that, it became clear to me that I wanted to live more simply. Sure, I still buy clothes and other items, but more often I'm giving away things and finding ways to make my life less complicated. This following quote by Einstein resonates deeply in my heart.

Out of clutter, find simplicity.
From discord, find harmony.
In the middle of difficulty lies opportunity.
—ALBERT EINSTEIN

When we have chaos, clutter and imbalance in our lives, including in our homes, we feel stressed out and chaotic in our minds. Here is something I've done for years that might interest you. I invite a guest over to my house, at least weekly; it helps motivate me to clean my home and consistently get rid of clutter and the nonessentials. I also tell my guest he or she can have anything in the pile of stuff I'm giving away.

When making simple or complicated decisions or choices in my life, I often use "peace" and "love" as my barometers. I ask myself: "Will making this choice bring *more peace* into my life, or *diminish* my level of peace?" Put another way, in each situation, ask whether each of your thoughts, words and deeds create a greater or lesser awareness of love and peace. Another valuable question I ask myself when I'm feeling stressed out about something: "Will this be an issue for me in six months?" Usually the answer is "no."

One of the most powerful life lessons I have come to understand in my life is the importance of simplifying outer things so that my inner life can take the driver's seat. Living an uncluttered life gives me time for the things I really care about, like time to think, to read, to walk in nature, to meditate and commune with God and to watch the sunrise or sunset. Through simplification, I am more clear-minded, and, I believe, a kinder, more sensitive person. When there is time to meditate, walk, read, reflect, think, pray and be in the simplicity and beauty of nature, then life has a more natural flow, which is very much like meditation. Life becomes meditation. The Divine becomes perfect simplicity.

Munificent with her love and kindness and inspiring with her compassion and optimistic attitude, my mom was my greatest teacher. One of the many lessons I learned from her was to "lighten up"—especially when life is difficult and pitches us curves. She'd often say to me, "This, too, shall pass" (a phrase used by Abraham Lincoln and also found in 1 Corinthians 10:12). Mom was always right. To use a baseball analogy, with a little faith, trust and patience, we can all hit home runs. Never let the fear of striking out keep you from playing the game and giving it your best, guided by your highest vision.

The actor and author Tyler Perry sums up one beautiful and effective way to simplify your life and to put the focus on what really matters when he said this:

> **It doesn't matter if a million people tell you what you can't do, or if ten million people tell you no. If you get one YES from God, that's ALL you need.**

I want to close this part of the book by sharing with you a passage I read recently in a wonderful out-of-print-book, *The Simple Life*, by Joan Atwater.

> *Our lives are over-burdened, and living often seems to us a terribly complicated affair. The problems of the world are so incredibly complex and we see that there are no simple answers. The complexity always leaves us with a feeling of helplessness and powerlessness. And still, amazingly enough, we go on, day by day, always half subconsciously yearning for something simpler, something more meaningful.*
>
> *So how we look at our lives and living becomes tremendously important. It's up to us to bring this authenticity, this simplicity, this directness, this unburdened clarity into our looking. If such a thing as living life fully interests you, then it's up to you to learn about it and live it.*

May you come to know and experience Love as your ever-present companion and beacon in your life's journey. Choose to embrace the fullness of life with élan and aplomb, and welcome a sacred balance. My wish is that you thrive day in, day out. I salute your great adventure and wish you joy, peace, happiness, and vibrant health.

*I no longer become angry. I not only do not say angry
words, I do not even think angry thoughts! If someone
does an unkind thing to me, I feel only compassion
instead of resentment. Even upon those who cause
suffering, I look with deep compassion, knowing
the harvest of sorrow that lies in store for them. If
there were those who hated me, I would love them
in return, knowing that hatred can only be overcome
by love, and knowing that there is good in all human
beings which can be reached by a loving approach.*

—PEACE PILGRIM

*Whatever you can do or dream, begin it!
Boldness has genius, power, and magic to it.*

—JOHANN WOLFGANG VON GOETHE

*The best way for us to keep fit and healthy is for us to
watch what we eat and think. Our choices of thoughts
and food are the major parts of either poor health or good
health. Life has given us unlimited choices and it's up
to us to educate ourselves on what really works for us.*

—LOUISE L. HAY

*A thorough study of the Bible shows us that the
men and women who God used in mighty ways
always had the attitude of celebrating what God
had done. They did not take His goodness for
granted, but they openly showed appreciation and
thankfulness for little things as well as big ones.*

—JOYCE MEYER

HUMOR  TIME

Each time you open a book and read it,
a tree smiles knowing there's life after death.

You deserve someone who would jump
fences to be with you, not someone who is
on the fence about being with you.

Hard work beats talent; you're going to be tired
more often than your talented friends.

Life is like a dogsled team. If you aren't the
lead dog, the scenery never changes.

Success in almost any field depends more on
energy and drive than it does on intelligence. This
explains why we have so many stupid leaders.

A leader must have the courage to act
against an expert's advice.

At my elderly age, "getting lucky" means
finding my car in the parking lot.

I learned how to belly dance today. I didn't have
to do much. I just gave it a little shake and the
darn thing started dancing all on its own.

My age is very inappropriate for my behavior.

If a man speaks his mind in the forest
and no women is around to hear it,
is he still wrong?

OMG, I'm rich! Silver in the hair,
Gold in the teeth, Crystals in the kidneys,
Sugar in the blood, Lead in the butt,
Iron in the arteries, and an inexhaustible
supply of Natural Gas!

At my age, the only pole dancing I do is to
hold on to the safety bar in the bathtub.

At my age, rolling out of bed in the morning is
easy... Getting up off the floor is another story.

They say that age is all in your mind. The trick is
keeping it from creeping down into your body.

I don't do drugs or drink. At my age,
I get the same effect just standing up too fast.

With age comes new skills... you can laugh,
cough, sneeze, and pee all at the same time?

PART 4

Open Up to Prosperity: Turning Your Dreams Into Reality

The way for you to be happy and successful, to get more of the things you really want in life, is to get the combinations to the locks. Instead of spinning the dials of life hoping for a lucky break, as if you were playing a slot machine, you must instead study and emulate those who already have done what you want to do and achieved the results you want to achieve.

—Brian Tracy

PEOPLE OFTEN SAY WE CREATE OUR OWN REALITY. In fact, I've been suggesting it throughout this book. But what does that really mean? Let's explore how to turn our dreams into reality.

PUTTING OUR THOUGHTS TO WORK

In the 1970s, positive thinking became almost synonymous with success. In its early use in contexts such as Dale Carnegie's success courses, positive thinking meant using willpower and conscious, positive thoughts to achieve goals. Napoleon Hill's maxim for success, "What you can conceive and believe, you can achieve," was a popular positive thinking slogan. Never underestimate the Divine potential of positive thinking. Rightly employed, this power of the mind is a catalyst that makes possible a wondrous transformation in our lives. It was Ralph Waldo Emerson who said, "The good mind chooses what is positive, what is advancing—embraces the affirmative."

Positive thinking includes belief in our own self-worth and in the value of everyone else and every circumstance. Such positive belief leads to self-confidence, respect for others and a lifestyle based on strong values. Sometimes we slip into the habit of negative thinking because we feel discouraged, depressed, lonely, isolated or stressed. We all want fast and easy results. But life isn't like that. Life is meant to be a challenge, and one of its greatest lessons is that when our minds are full of fear, doubt and clutter, good ideas can't get through. The best ideas and best decisions come when we're relaxed and open to impressions and responsive to them. In that state, we can find a way to link the present situation with wonderful opportunities to learn and grow.

Don't try to sit in a chair and think positively about something and expect it to happen. Keeping alive a goal or dream, or even hope, requires action. You have to make it happen—or at least help make it happen.

TAKE CHARGE OF YOUR MIND & LIFE

You'll notice that successful people are very deliberate about choosing to be in charge of their lives. They don't get up in the morning and hope that they'll have a good day. High-achieving people take full control of their lives and, if they don't encounter the circumstances they want, they make them. Success and real fulfillment always begin with a dream. Successful people know nothing will happen unless they have the courage to start living their dream. This means taking risks, being vulnerable, making mistakes and even failing. Life can't be lived on the sidelines if you want to be successful. There's enormous fun, as well as risk, in challenging yourself to something you've always wanted to do.

Too often we live in our comfort zone instead of taking risks. How often did your mom tell you "Take a risk today, sweetie!" when she sent you off to school? Probably never. Most of us are taught from a very early age to play small and play it safe rather than to play big and expand our horizons. Our comfort zone can remain tiny all our lives unless we subject it to some growing pains.

The way we live reflects our thoughts, dreams, expectations, beliefs, hopes, feelings of self-worth and desires. We have free will to create our own happiness and our own heaven or hell. Here's a quick example of how we create our own reality: One of my clients, Kathleen, doesn't like where she lives but she can't afford to move. She resided in an old, noisy apartment building where her walls were in need of a fresh coat of paint, the windows hadn't been washed in years, and she didn't have any plants or other living things besides herself and her cat. It was no surprise to me that she was miserable, had a hard time sleeping, lacked energy and felt depressed. She complained about her surroundings often in our counseling sessions, but failed to do anything about it—until I presented her with a challenge and assignment. I explained to her that if she would simply paint some of the walls a soothing color such as soft green or pale blue, bring in some fresh flowers and plants and get a simple water fountain and perhaps a sound device (that plays the sounds of nature such a ocean

waves, gentle rain and singing birds, etc.,) to help block out the noisy neighbors, she would be much happier in her environment, sleep better and have a more positive attitude. And then I said that if she would do this in the next week, I would gift her with a dinner party and make all of the food for five of her favorite friends. Well, that put a smile on her face. In fact, she got so excited about these few changes—which cost less than $150.00—that she used a few days of vacation time at work to get the projects done within four days. During the dinner party, everyone loved her personal and physical changes, and we all could feel her energy shift. She had gone from feeling sad, depressed and enervated to being happy, hopeful and energetic.

What can you change in your immediate surroundings today, this week, this month that will also put a smile on your face and in your heart? Knowing this, you can consciously modify your inner states to create and live your highest potential and vision. You are not the victim of circumstances; you are the architect of your life. Your conscious thoughts create an unconscious image of your life, yourself and your feelings, and that unconscious image reproduces itself perfectly in your real-life circumstances.

When life gets complicated and we find ourselves with negative thoughts and feelings, it's tempting to think that it's the complications, conditions or people that upset us. But that's not the way it really works. It's only the way we think about the things that happen to us that cause our upsets. We can choose not to become upset. We really can. And as we change our thoughts and stop thinking of ourselves as victims, our lives shift and change in all kinds of positive ways.

HOW TO BREAK THE VICIOUS CYCLE OF NEGATIVE THINKING

Let's look at an all-too-common example of how the principle of choice works: weight control. Let's just assume that you've always had difficulty controlling your weight. You've tried all kinds of diets and they've never worked, so you have negative feelings about diets. You've tried to limit the amount of food you eat without much success, so you don't have much faith in your self-control. You get on the scale every morning and it reinforces your image of yourself as overweight. It really is a vicious cycle. In order to understand why you keep repeating the same patterns, you need to understand the way your mind works.

Brain researchers see the mind as composed of three primary parts: the conscious, the subconscious, and the superconscious. As your window to the world, the conscious mind runs your daily waking activities, such as making decisions, relating to others and doing your work. The subconscious mind, at the same time, carries memories of all your experiences. It is a storage-and-retrieval center for all the information your conscious mind sends it based on your daily experiences—essentially a computer that is fed the data of your every thought, feeling and experience. The superconscious mind is your connection to the Divine, to God

Relating this to the example of weight control, if you get up every morning and worry about what clothes will fit, if you dread getting on your scale, if you dislike being seen in public, if you think about going on a diet but doubt that it will work (they don't— I've written about that extensively in my books *Living on the Lighter Side* and *Invest in Yourself with Exercise*), you are programming your subconscious computer with negative thoughts. Your subconscious mind creates reality according to its programming. If you think of yourself as being fat, having little self-control, or being unable to change, you will see those beliefs reflected in your life—and you won't lose a pound.

The same is true for every other area of your life. Your subconscious beliefs and thoughts about yourself, your relationships with others, your money, your material possessions, your job and so on, will be faithfully re-created in your life. You may be thinking, "No, that isn't true for me: I know that I really want to lose weight and tone up my body (or make more money, or have a really good relationship), but I am not experiencing it in my life." The answer lies in the vast difference between wanting something on the conscious level and wanting it on the subconscious level.

The conscious mind and the subconscious mind are often in conflict. Consciously you may want something, yet subconsciously you create mediocrity or failure. That's why positive thinking as it's commonly perceived doesn't work. As I lecture around the country and the world, I often hear statements such as, "I continually affirm, visualize, meditate and believe in my highest good, but I rarely see results." It doesn't do much good to force yourself to think positive thoughts if your subconscious still harbors many negative beliefs. What you need to do is to reprogram your subconscious mind to break the vicious cycle of negative beliefs creating your negative reality. In order to do this, you must make some behavior changes on a conscious level that will contribute to new beliefs.

The birth of excellence begins with our awareness that our beliefs are a choice. We can choose beliefs that limit us, or we can choose beliefs that support us. The key is to choose beliefs that are conducive to success and to discard the ones that hold you back. Beliefs can turn on or shut off the flow of ideas. Our beliefs are what determine how much of our potential we'll be able to tap. Virgil, one of the greatest poets of ancient Rome, said, "They can because they think they can."

WHAT YOU THINK ABOUT YOU BRING ABOUT

In the Bible, Proverbs 23:7 we find this: "For as a man thinks in his heart, so he is." In the world of metaphysics (meaning beyond physical matter), there is an unwritten law of correspondence supporting the Bible quote that says, "As within, so without." The way I explain this in my workshops is that we are always attracting to ourselves the equivalency of what we think, how we feel and what we believe. Ralph Waldo Emerson said that... *we become what we think about all day long.* It's true. In other words, your outer world tends to be a reflection of your inner (subconscious) world—like a mirror. What you see in the world around you will be consistent over time with the world inside you.

Studies reveal that successful, happy people think about successful, happy things most of the time. By the same token, unsuccessful, unhappy people concentrate their thoughts on people they dislike, situations they are angry about and events that they do not wish to take place in their lives. These data point directly to the law of concentration, which says, "Whatever you dwell upon grows in your reality." These ideas come from all of the great teachers in life—from the central figure in the Christian religion, Jesus, to other teachers like Socrates, Pythagoras, Thoreau, Emerson, Whitman and so many more, including current teachers such as Joel Osteen and Joyce Meyer. If you read my book *Body Temple Vitality,* you are aware of these "laws of the universe" that have come down through the ages and, when implemented in our lives, will transform us if we embrace them.

These two laws in combination explain much of success and most of failure. Whatever we think about most of the time, we bring about in our lives.

So the starting point in making your dreams a reality is to discipline yourself to think and talk about only those things you want in your life, and to refuse to think and talk about anything other than what you want. These can be intangible as well as tangible things. Besides thinking and talking about the new job or material things you desire, talk and think about healthy things, such as being grateful. Try being loving instead of angry. Push aside all of that negativity—all of those fears, doubts and self-sabotaging, limiting thoughts and visions—and you will discover that all manner of remarkable things happen in your life that bring you closer to your dreams.

It's equally important to feel the feeling of the dream fulfilled, of whatever it is you desire, whether it's being prosperous, fit and healthy; being in a loving, supportive relationship; or being very successful at work. If you start acting a certain way, you eventually become that way. The key to the process is to capture the feeling, because when you do that you've captured the ability to internalize your idea, and then it's only a matter of time. Feeling refers to the intensity or amount of emotion that accompanies your mental pictures.

Emotion is central to all accomplishments. You might want to remember the following: T x F = R: Thought times Feeling equals

Positive Thoughts Generate Positive Feelings and Attract Positive Life Experiences

Realization. The thought or picture multiplied by the feeling or emotion that accompanies it equals the speed at which it occurs in your reality. This is something I created over 30 years ago to help my clients remember how important are their thoughts and feelings when they desire to create miracles in their lives.

My extensive research, as well as my own experience, has taught me to appreciate the importance of feelings. I like to describe emotion as an electromagnetic force field so strong that it sends up a vibration and pulls like vibrations to itself. It is a magnet for similar energy.

After interviewing many highly intelligent, successful people with diverse backgrounds and vast experience, I came to the conclusion that what we think about, and how we feel about the things we think about, are the determining factors in the way our life works out.

If we are thinking positive thoughts but not getting positive results, most of the time it's because the emotional channels have not been opened. This can be done by practicing forgiveness toward ourselves and others and by passionately releasing fear, anger, guilt and any other feelings that block the presence of love, of God, inside us.

When we see our world only according to what surrounds us right now, we limit what we are going to have. Instead of thinking "I'll believe it when I see it," try thinking "I'll see it when I believe it."

In order for this process to work, you must also get in the habit of saying what it is you desire. Be specific. Specifically plant in your mind that which you choose to bring into your life. You see, the creative principle works according to the seeds you plant. If you plant scarcity, disease and disaster, you get back scarcity, disease and disaster. If you plant love, you get back love. Say what you want, be specific, and act as if what you want is already true. That's key.

Any feelings we want we can have, if we think intensely enough. Try it. It's remarkable, and it's true. We can even feel cool when it's hot or friendly when we'd rather be alone if we use our minds to paint the picture vividly enough. It's this powerful force of feeling, drawn into the subconscious mind, which acts as a generator to create what we desire.

POSITIVE ACTIONS BRING POSITIVE RESULTS

Here are some positive actions you can take to change your circumstances.

- If you feel that your beliefs about money are creating negative results in your life, examine the behaviors that support those negative beliefs. Maybe you are frugal in your grocery shopping, conscious of buying the cheapest brands and skipping the luxuries. Although frugality might be wise in light of your current financial situation, you should be aware that it also tends to reinforce your belief that you have very little money. One way to attack this belief is to substitute a new behavior for the old one. For example, the next time you're in a grocery store, allow yourself to indulge in a little luxury. While you're doing it, imagine that this capacity to indulge a little is your present reality, and feel it.

- If your problem is loneliness, make it a point to smile at one stranger every day, just as if you had plenty of friends and an abundance of love to share.

- If you are heavier than you want to be, buy yourself something appealing that you would normally have denied yourself because of your present appearance.

PUT WINGS UNDER YOUR SELF-ESTEEM

It's important to understand that living your vision and creating what your heart desires is related to how you feel about yourself. If you feel unworthy, it will be almost impossible for abundance to flow into your life. If you feel that you are important enough to ask and Divine enough to receive, receiving will be your reward. "Think of how a tree unfolds to all of its magnificent potential, always reaching for the sunshine and growing and flourishing," writes Wayne Dyer in *Change Your Thoughts—Change Your Life*. "Would you ever suggest to a tree, 'You should be ashamed of yourself for having that disgusting moss on your bark and for letting your limbs grow crooked?' Of course not. A tree allows the Life Force to work through it. You have the power within your thoughts to be as natural as the tree." He reminds us that all we need to do is to be ourselves.

WHAT YOU GIVE AWAY, YOU GET BACK MULTIPLIED

Another important aspect of changing your subconscious energy involves the law of circulation, which states that what you give away, you get—multiplied. You must first give away the very thing you desire. If you desire increased prosperity in your life, for instance, don't hoard it, because that would be manifesting a fear that there might not be enough. Share what you have with others and feel how the world begins to open to you as well.

Once you decide what you want, begin tithing. Tithing traditionally means to give a tenth of your income to your church, but tithing doesn't necessarily have to go to a church—and it doesn't have to be 10 percent. Tithe gifts can be in monetary form or a giving of yourself in time and/or deposits of love. I tithe money to my church every month and to those who feed my soul and nourish my spirituality and who are making a positive difference on this planet, whether they are individuals or organizations. I also give money and time to people less fortunate than I. Remember, though, it's futile to say, "Yes, when such-and-such money comes in, I will give a tenth of it as a tithe." You have to start helping those in need before that, acting in the spirit of "give that you may receive."

One day, after writing my prosperity affirmations and goals on cards, I went to the grocery store. While waiting in the checkout line, I suddenly called out to the harried mother with two crying babies in front of me who didn't have enough to cover all of her groceries, "I'll pay for those." Needless to say, she was astonished! Quite honestly, so was I; the words seemed to have just popped out of my mouth. After some hesitancy on her part and some impressive cajolery on mine, she let me pay her bill. The pleasure I received made me feel rich inside. Later that same day, I ran into a person in Santa Monica whom I had counseled several months before. At that time she had been unable to pay, and I had written the sessions off as a good learning experience. This day, seemingly out of the blue, she wrote me a check for twice the amount she owed me, saying that my guidance had a profound, positive effect on her life. I shouldn't have been surprised, because I had "acted as if."

To "act as if" takes courage and trust. It's hard to start giving when you don't think you have enough, unless you act as if. Go out into the world as if you had the courage, and you'll find that the courage you wanted is already there. Do the thing, and the power is yours. Yes, it begins with a risk, but if you don't risk, you don't receive. That's how you generate power.

Your subconscious mind is extraordinarily powerful, but it is a servant, not a master. It coordinates every aspect of your thoughts, feelings, behaviors, words, actions and emotions to fit a pattern consistent with your dominant mental pictures. It guides you to engage in the behaviors that will move you ever closer to achieving the goals you visualize and feel most of the time. If you visualize something that you fear, your subconscious mind will accept that as a command, too. It will then use its marvelous powers to bring your fears, instead of your dreams and aspirations, into reality.

Many people feel that their deepest beliefs and motivations are forever a mystery to them. They feel they don't understand the real reasons behind their actions, and as a result they feel powerless to change their actions. They have it backwards: we all have the ability to recognize our beliefs through our actions, and to change them by changing our actions. Although beliefs may seem mysterious and complicated on a conscious level, on a subconscious level they are usually simple. Our beliefs about ourselves are based entirely on our past experiences. All of our experiences program our subconscious, and the result is what we are today.

That is not to say that all you will ever be is the sum of your experiences. Maybe you've noticed at some time or other that your life experiences are all very similar—it's just the people involved who keep changing. You can change that pattern by choosing to feed different programming into your subconscious computer.

CHOOSE YOUR THOUGHTS & WORDS WISELY

Two very effective ways to reprogram your subconscious mind are creative visualizations and affirmations. The idea is to alter your state of consciousness in such a way that you can temporarily set aside the conscious mind and concentrate specifically on the subconscious. According to brain researchers, suggestions given to your subconscious while in this altered state, whether they are images or affirmations, will be at least 20 times as effective as suggestions given in a normal state of consciousness. One of the best ways to alter or slow down your state of consciousness or brain wave activity is through relaxed deep breathing.

It's very helpful to feed your mind a clear mental picture of your desired goals for the coming day, the coming week and the coming months just before going to sleep at night. I do this every night for about 10 minutes. As you drop off to sleep, your brain wave activity naturally slows down and your subconscious mind is the most receptive to the input of new commands. Since your mental pictures are a command, take those last few minutes before you fall asleep to daydream and fantasize about exactly the person you want to be and the life you want to have. Your subconscious mind will then take the pictures down into its laboratory and work on them all night long. What often happens is that you wake up in the morning with ideas and insights that will help make those things you visualized a part of your life.

Most people have only vague, fuzzy pictures of what they want. They say they want to be rich or healthy or happy. But when you ask them exactly what that means to them, they don't really know. In my book *Invest in Yourself with Exercise,* I emphasize the importance of vividness in mental pictures. The more vividly you can see something that you want in your mind's eye, the more rapidly it will materialize in your reality.

Vividness requires precision and clarity of detail in your mental pictures. Spend some time examining your desired goals, drawing pictures of them either actually or mentally, or writing out clear descriptions of what your wishes would look like when they came true. Complex pictures will be accepted by your subconscious as a command, and your subconscious mind will go immediately to work to coordinate all your other resources, internal and external, to bring those goals into your life.

Be precise. Be absolutely definite. Know what you want, visualize what you want and say what you want. It will not do to say you want a lot of money or that you want a new car or a house. You must state exactly what it is that you want and hold that picture steadily before you, so strongly that you can feel the wish fulfilled.

If you want money, state definitely how much you want. It must be a definite sum. If prosperity is your goal, make part of your visualization definite plans for the good you will do with the prosperity you create for yourself and others. I always end my visualization with this phrase to God, knowing my life is in God's hand and He knows what's best for me: *"This or something better I now accept and give thanks for in my life."*

Your visualizations can be turned into affirmations by making them real and vivid in your mind. Write down your major goals in the present tense on three-by-five cards, one to a card, and review them on a regular basis. Read the goal—for example, "I have 30 minutes each day for myself"—then close your eyes, breathe deeply, relax for a few seconds and imagine what it would be like if you did indeed have those 30 minutes. Visualize some of the specific ways your life would change. Feel the feeling of calm and groundedness that comes with that extra time. Then open your eyes, smile and go about your business, knowing in your mind's eye that you have already succeeded in achieving your goal.

Years ago, one of my goals and dreams was to have a home-away-from-home, somewhere out in a natural setting where I could go to write and have some quiet and solitude. Although I wasn't sure where I wanted this home to be, I was very clear on some of my specific requirements: I wanted it to be a long way from a large city and crowds of people, and surrounded by trees and nature's sounds. The home itself needed to made of wood and windows, have a spectacular view, and lend itself to my healthy lifestyle—sun, fresh air, organic garden, and space to work out. So for a few months I visualized this home. I wrote my vision down on three-by-five index cards and gave thanks to God that it was already a reality.

About six months later, I was invited to give a seven-day workshop in another coastal town far from my home in Brentwood (West Los Angeles/Santa Monica). I had been there before, speaking at different churches and local hospitals. I had always thought it was a beautiful area but had never considered buying a home there. One evening I had a break during my workshop and was invited to visit some friends who lived on top of a forested hill overlooking the Pacific Ocean. During our conversation in their home, they mentioned that the house next door was for sale. I answered casually and didn't give the information any more thought until later: in the middle of the night I was hit by God's loving, cosmic two-by-four and immediately realized I was supposed to buy that house next door to my friends. The realization seemed absurd, because I hadn't even looked at the inside of the house. I simply knew it was meant to be mine, and that it would be the perfect place for personal retreats and writing.

The next morning I called my friends. They were delighted with my decision, even though they thought I was a little crazy! I called the realtor, and learned that the house was already in escrow, about to close. He would be happy to show me other homes, he said, but this one was no longer available. I told him, "You don't seem to understand. That's my home and I'm not interested in looking at any others." I left my telephone number and asked him to call me when the house was available. You can guess how the story turned out: it did become available, I made an offer, and it became my retreat home.

It certainly didn't come without roadblocks—the path of least resistance isn't always the best one. The whole process of creating my home presented me with one challenge after another and taught me numerous lessons as well, such as the importance of belief and faith and not judging by appearances; such as being thankful for everything seen and unseen, and beholding the Divine in everyone and everything. By the way, my home-away-from-home was on top of a hill, surrounded by trees, overlooking the ocean, had lots of light, and was filled with angels, just as I visualized it. I had never thought about that specific location, but I knew it was the perfect place for me and was made possible because of my focused desire for it. I enjoyed that home for 21 years and then made the decision to let someone else enjoy this beautiful home because I was ready to move on to new and even greater adventures in my life and to create another home of my dreams.

TAKE A WORD INVENTORY

Like most of us, from time to time I get into bad habits with words. Not too long ago, I was driving with David Craddock in Santa Monica. The day was hot and the traffic was heavy. A rude, reckless driver cut me off. I said in a loud voice, "I hate it when someone does that to me!" David looked very startled. He said, "Don't use the 'H' word. That's a terrible thing to put into your consciousness. Try instead, 'I prefer drivers not to cut me off in traffic,' and then silently bless the driver."

I was in no mood to listen to a lecture. I felt like saying to him, "I hate it when somebody lectures me!" But I didn't do that, because David was absolutely correct. Have you ever said, "That burns me up," "They're driving me crazy," or "This is back-breaking work"? These seemingly harmless expressions program garbage into your subconscious mind. The subconscious does not know that you don't really mean it. It plants those ideas in your experience storage vault and plays them out into your life as if you really meant what you said. Just as an injurious diet weakens the body, leading inevitably to disease, a regimen of negative thoughts and words debilitates the mind and soul, fostering unhappiness and an unfulfilled life.

Take an inventory of everything you say during the course of the day. Be aware of the words you use. Speak only those words that are positive, loving and uplifting, and that represent what you want for yourself. Remember, as mentioned earlier from Philippians 4: 8–9…

Whatever is true,
whatever is honorable,
whatever is just,
whatever is pure,
whatever is lovely,
whatever is gracious,
if there is any excellence,
if there is anything worthy of praise,
think about these things.

I've learned to pay attention to what I say (most of the time) and to interrupt negative expressions. When I find myself straying toward negativity, I usually say or think to myself "cancel" or "erase" and then change the words. I have also imagined in my mind's eye a large screen on which I write any negative expressions I've used and then draw an X through them. I have done this on paper, too, and then burned the paper. Use any method that is effective for you.

It can be a real challenge to find positive ways to say exactly what you mean. But it certainly can be done. For instance, notice how often you say "I'm sorry" and try "I apologize" instead. After all, that is what you mean. Change "I'm afraid you have the wrong number" to "You have the wrong number." For "I hate it when my boss is in a bad mood," try "I prefer a cheerful workplace." As you find more positive ways to speak more accurately, you stop feeding your subconscious mind misinformation about yourself. In my book *Affirming God's Love,* to help you speak and write in a more positive light, I have a chapter which includes my favorite *260 Positive Words*.

Make Your Word Gold

You are as good as your word. In my opinion, when it comes to keeping your word, there is no such thing as a small situation. Perhaps it's no big deal to say we're going to call someone and then not do it, but it can be very important to the other person. It's very important to me that my friends and business associates be accountable—that their words count. When I learn that someone doesn't follow through on what they say they're going to do, and it's apparent that this is a pattern, I choose not to spend time with that person. To me, a verbal agreement is as serious and binding as a written one. In fact, I have verbal agreements, as opposed to written ones, with most of the companies for which I do consulting. People know my word is gold and they can always count on me.

I'm very inspired by people who make their word count. My mom, June, was always a shining example for me on the importance of keeping your word. Every time she made a promise, no matter how small or seemingly insignificant, she kept her word. If she made plans with someone and then was offered the opportunity to do something more exciting or interesting, she never hesitated one second before she would say, "Thank you, I'd love to do it, but I already have a commitment." June's behavior invariably brought two reactions, both positive. The first friend was pleased because she and June did whatever they were going to do, and the second friend was impressed with her integrity. June was not only well-liked, she was also very successful. She was as good as her word. To me, there can be no higher praise than that.

> Make your word count. It's a gift you give to your family, friends, business associates, community and the world.

In a study conducted at Sussex University, subjects viewed a selection of television news broadcasts. The topics were positive, negative or neutral. Not surprisingly, negative news broadcasts left the subjects in a bad mood and made most of them edgy. We always have a choice about what we look at and to what we give our attention. So reinforce positive thoughts, words and actions by what you watch, and avoid putting your attention on negativity. Thoughts embroiled in negativity tarnish your perception of the beauties and miracles of life. Fill not only your conversation but your consciousness with positive things. Surmount all life's challenges by following your heart and letting the Divine wisdom within you guide you to the realization of your dreams.

PATIENT PERSISTENCE IN THE GOOD

There's an unfathomable, yet recognizable, Divine Order to this universe. God is Omnipotent, Omniscient and Omnipresent—always working in alignment with what we need for our highest good and spiritual unfolding and growth. I've learned not to analyze or question this loving presence anymore, which asks only for our trust, faith and courage.

You are exactly where you need to be in life. At any moment you can choose to experience something else, simply by taking responsibility and consciously choosing to think differently. In the fantastic words of Zorba the Greek writer Nikos Kanzantzakis, "You have your paintbrush and colors. Paint paradise, and in you go."

*Hope is one of the best ways to shed light
on the process of unfolding miracles—and
it's part of the ongoing miracle itself.*

—THOMAS KINKADE

*We have a body and we take care of it. We exercise,
feed and bathe it. We have a mind and most of us
exercise that, too. We read, write and think. But
we also are a soul and if we don't nourish the soul,
we won't be vibrantly healthy or complete.*

—SUSAN SMITH JONES

*If the only prayer you ever say in your life
is 'Thank you,' this would suffice.*

—MEISTER ECKHART

*The most intelligent way to move in the
direction of a good life is to live each day,
each experience, as authentically as we can,
with integrity, honesty and courage.*

—ALEXANDRA STODDARD

HUMOR  TIME

*A man's health can be judged by which he
takes two at a time—pills or stairs.*
—Joan Welsh

*If you can't afford a doctor, go to an airport—
you'll get a free x-ray and a breast exam, and if you
mention Al Qaeda, you'll get a free colonoscopy.*

*I'm not crazy. I'm just special. No, wait…
maybe I'm crazy. One second… I have to
talk to myself about this, hold on…*

I am in shape! Round is a shape.

*If walking were good for your health, the postman would
be immortal. A whale swims all day, only eats fish, only
drinks water and is fat. A rabbit only eats vegetables, runs
and hops all day long and only lives 5 years. A tortoise
doesn't run and does nothing energetic, yet it lives for
45 years. And you tell me to exercise! I don't think so.*

*Men are like wine. Some turn to vinegar,
but the best improve with age.*
—Pope John XXII

*Just remember, once you're over the hill,
you begin to pick up speed.*
—Charles Schulz

*Dear Life, I have a complete grasp on the fact that you
are not fair. So please stop teaching me that lesson.*

*I don't know why people are so keen to put
the details of their private life in public: they
forget that invisibility is a superpower.*

*Smile... it will either warm their heart or
piss them off... either way you win!*

*Stay away from negative people; they
have a problem for every solution.*

*At age 20, we worry about what others think of us.
At 40, we don't care what they think of us. At 60,
we discover they haven't been thinking of us at all.*

—ANN LANDERS

*So far, you've survived 100% of your
worst days. This, too, shall pass.*

*Almost everything will work again if you unplug
it for a few minutes... including you.*

—ANNE LAMOTT

*I think I need glasses because I keep seeing
a lot of people with two faces.
Not every person is going to understand you and
that's okay. They have a right to their opinion
and you have every right to ignore it.*

—JOEL OSTEEN

Afterword

THANK YOU FOR TAKING TIME TO READ THIS BOOK. I hope in some way, through the pages of this book, I have inspired and motivated you to make positive changes in your personal health program and holistic lifestyle, and to cherish and celebrate your life each and every day. Here are some of my final thoughts about physical, mental and spiritual well-being that I'll leave with you as you embark on your thriving adventure—your life.

Life is all about the choices we make day in, day out. Living our best life means choosing to appreciate our magnificent bodies. The body is sacred, a temple of the living, loving God, and therefore deserves reverence. Treat yourself with respect. Don't wait until you're sick to recognize the miracle of your body. Honor the love inside you and the love you are.

If you want to become healthier and more powerful, begin with how you feel about yourself and accept your body as a temple. Heaven on earth is inside each one of us at this moment. In your unique body, mind and spirit, you have been given everything you need to be the best you can be, to thrive in your health and life. So cherish and respect your body unconditionally—no matter what its current shape—because it is sacred.

As a divine being, made in the image and likeness of God, you deserve tender, loving care. We may find this difficult to accept, especially where our bodies are concerned. Many of us need to learn to be a friend to our bodies. Getting mad at our bodies only makes matters worse. Although they are but temporary homes for our spiritual beings, we must still take care of them because they are sacred vessels for this voyage on earth. Love your body and be committed to staying fit for your life journey.

Start today by tuning in more attentively to your body. It is a fantastic feedback machine. If you listen, you will discover that it communicates very well. When you get a headache, your body is trying to tell you something. Listen to your body's signals. The key is your willingness to listen and act. If you feel pain, what is your body trying to tell you? It may be telling you that you're eating too much, or eating the wrong kinds of food, or smoking or drinking too much, or not sleeping enough, or not drinking enough water or getting enough exercise. It could be telling you that you need to get outside more to play and pray, or that there's too much emotional congestion in your life.

Listen to your body. Respect and appreciate it. Take loving care of it. You will learn to discern what your body is trying to tell you. And please, choose your doctor carefully. Choose someone who practices a wellness lifestyle and who listens to you. There is a tendency today for doctors to turn to technology and all kinds of elaborate testing first, or to prescribe a regimen of medications, before listening to you or to their own intuition. I don't think it's a good trend.

As you think about your health and health care, ask yourself both of these questions: what can the doctor do for me? And, how can I help myself? You are the authority on your body. Educate yourself. If you have specific health conditions, read up on them online and figure out how to get the best possible care. And remember this: It is normal to be healthy. It's your divine birthright to be well. **Choose wisely and show by your daily actions that you are a champion of creating your best, healthiest life.**

Before I conclude this Afterword and the book, I wanted to take an opportunity to share with you, my valued reader, something about my God-centered life and how my Christian faith intertwines in my personal and professional life.

Living a faith-centered life is my #1 health and vitality secret. Each morning, before I exercise, I first begin my day by reading a passage from the Bible and then meditate on what I just perused. This sacred, morning practice starts my day off on a positive, peaceful note and fills me with joy and serenity. I let God's love shine forth from me into all of my activities for the day and evening. Connecting to God each morning, and other times during the day, reinforces in me that I can choose to thrive and live a peaceful, balanced life, and it begins with my thoughts and what I put my attention on throughout the day.

As mentioned previously in the book, one of my favorite Bible passages is found in Philippians 4:8-9:

"Whatever is true, whatever is honorable, whatever is just, whatever is pure, whatever is lovely, whatever is gracious, if there is any excellence, if there is anything worthy of praise, think about these things. Whatever you have learned and received and heard and seen in me, do; and the God of peace will be with you."

Daily, I aspire to take loving care of my body temple given to me as a gift from God, and to celebrate the joy of living with as many people as possible in my work and experiences.

Resources

Please refer to **www.SusanSmithJones.com** to learn more about, or to purchase, these books. You will find the full list of Susan's titles on her website.

Living on the Lighter Side

The Curative Kitchen & Lifestyle

Healthy, Happy & Radiant . . . at Any Age

Wired to Meditate
(Audio Book)

Choose to Live Peacefully
(Audio Book)

Vegetable Soup/The Fruit Bowl
(Co-authored with Dianne Warren
for children ages 1–8)

Body Temple Vitality

Affirming God's Love

Invest in Yourself with Exercise

God-Centered Health

About
Susan Smith Jones, PhD

FOR A WOMAN WITH THREE OF AMERICA'S AND THE UK'S MOST ORDINARY NAMES, **Dr. Susan Smith Jones** has certainly made extraordinary contributions in the fields of holistic health, longevity, optimum nutrition, high-level fitness and balanced, peaceful living. For starters, she taught students, staff and faculty at UCLA how to be healthy and fit for 30 years!

Susan is the founder and president of Health Unlimited, a Los Angeles-based consulting firm dedicated to optimal wellness and holistic health education. As a renowned motivational speaker, Susan travels internationally as a frequent radio/TV talk show guest and motivational speaker (seminars, workshops, lectures and keynote address); she's also the author of more than 2,500 magazine articles and over 30 books, including—*The Curative Kitchen & Lifestyle*; *Living on the Lighter Side*; *Healthy, Happy & Radiant… at Any Age*; *Invest in Yourself with Exercise*, *Affirming God's Love* and *Body Temple Vitality*.

Susan is in a unique position to testify on the efficacy of her basic message that health is the result of choice. When her back was fractured in an automobile accident, her physician told her that she would never be able to carry "anything heavier than a small purse." Susan chose not to accept this verdict; within six months, there was no longer any pain or evidence of the fracture. Soon, she fully regained her health and active lifestyle. Susan attributes her healing to her natural-foods diet, a daily well-rounded fitness program, a strong God- and faith-centered life, along with the power of determination, balanced living and a deep commitment to expressing her highest potential. Since that time, she has been constantly active in spreading the message that anyone can choose radiant health and rejuvenation. Her inspiring message and innovative techniques for achieving total health in body, mind and spirit have won her a grateful and enthusiastic following and have put her in constant demand internationally as a health and fitness consultant and educator. A gifted teacher, Susan brings together modern research and ageless wisdom in all of her work. When she's not traveling the world, she resides in both West Los Angeles and England.

How the Sunflower Inspires Susan

When I look at a Sunflower, I can't help but to think of God's love and light, power and energy, in my life, and also how we can all choose to thrive each day by incorporating the following principles into our lives:

To stand tall and follow our dreams; to always focus on the positive; to show kindness to others; to be our own best friend; to be the best we can be and to consistently remember to celebrate the miracle of YOU and life itself.

NOTES

Made in the USA
Monee, IL
13 May 2022

96357097R10090

If you enjoyed this book, please visit: **SusanSmithJones.com**, **ChristianLifestyleMatters.com** and **BooksToUplift.com** for more details on Susan and her work. Her books and websites are like having a "holistic health app" for anything related to holistic health and living a faith- and God-centered life.

> If you'd like to receive Susan's free monthly *Healthy Living Newsletters* filled with uplifting, empowering and high-powered information, go to **SusanSmithJones.com** and sign-up on the page Subscribe & Win! It takes only 15 seconds and you will also receive several gifts from Susan.

We need to find God, and He cannot be found in noise and restlessness. God is the friend of silence.

—MOTHER TERESA

Affirm the inherent goodness of living by saying thank you.

—THOMAS KINKADE

The doctor of the future will give no medicine, but will interest his patients in the care of the human frame, in diet, and in the cause and prevention of disease.

—THOMAS A. EDISON

Cherish the music that stirs in your heart, the beauty that forms in your mind, the loveliness that drapes in your purest thoughts, for out of them will grow all delightful conditions, all heavenly environments; of these, if you but remain true to them, your world will at last be built.

—JAMES ALLEN

It's not easy being grateful all the time. But it's when you feel least thankful that you are most in need of what gratitude can give you.

—OPRAH WINFREY

One of the most important keys to effective prayer is approaching God as His friend. A friendship involves loving and being loved. It means knowing that God is on your side, wanting to help you, cheering you on and always keeping your best interest in mind. God loves you and desires your friendship!

—JOYCE MEYER

Sunflowers:
Their Meaning & Symbology

WHILE NOT A RARE FLOWER, the Sunflower is still a beautiful symbol of power for many people. In many ways, it's more powerful in what it symbolizes because it is easy to grow in your backyard or a patio container.

In my 20s, I was given the nickname "Sunny" because of how much I relished this sunny, happy gem, the Sunflower, and how I always took (and still do to this day) a positive approach to life. So this is why I chose to begin and end this book with glorious sunflowers.

Meaning of the Sunflower

The sunflower has developed unique meanings across the world, and many cultures share similar views of the flower thanks to its physical characteristics. Some of the most common meanings include:

- Long life, mainly since most varieties stand in full bloom for months on end during the hottest days of summer

- Feelings of adoration, admiration and platonic love towards a person, such as a family member or friend

- Loyalty and strong bonds between two people, as represented by the strong and upright stem

- Seeking out positivity and strength, as the bloom turns to face the sun

- Nourishing yourself and others, since the sunflower produces an abundance of edible seeds

- Brightening your mood, through the vibrancy of the yellow or orange petals

- Good fortune and lasting happiness

Etymological Meaning of the Sunflower

The English name for the Sunflower is quite literal and taken from its bright sun-like appearance. Its scientific name, Helianthus, is just as literal because it combines the two Greek words for sun and flower.

Symbolism of the Sunflower

It's no surprise that both ancient and modern people associated the Sunflower with warmth, positivity, power, strength and happiness since it bears such a strong resemblance to the Sun itself. In Greek mythology, it's tied to a story of a nymph who becomes the flower after losing her love. Victorian flower language ascribes a meaning of gratitude to the dwarf Sunflower, while it's considered a good luck charm for occasions like graduations and new businesses in China. Of course, Sunflowers also feature prominently in works from artists like Van Gogh.

Sunflower Facts

- The Sunflower is native to North America, but it has spread across the world through export.

- Native Americans planted wild varieties as a source of food, but modern breeding has emphasized petal size and count over seed production in many varieties.

- The Sunflower can range in height from six inches to over 12 feet tall, depending on the variety.

Botanical Characteristics of the Sunflower

Aside from being beautiful and important symbolically, the Sunflower is downright useful. Almost all varieties produce edible and delicious seeds (and you can grow salubrious green sprouts from the seeds) with loads of health benefits, especially when eaten raw (not roasted or salted). If you don't eat the seeds yourself, you can feed your local songbirds just by letting the seeds dry on the stalk. The entire plant also produces a pale yellow dye.